Mind, Body and Electromagnetism

After an early life dominated by music, and then graduating in mathematics, the author has been careful to avoid the specialist career. A number of years were spent in teaching, and further years in technological design and commerce. Eventually he was able to divide his time between industrial projects and private research. This book represents a summary of about twelve years of study into aspects of physiology, psychology, and Eastern philosophy, together with practical experimentation into the electromagnetics of the body. During the last two years, he has been active in political debate, expressing concern about the revival of Darwinian attitudes—also touched upon in this book. The author is married with four children.

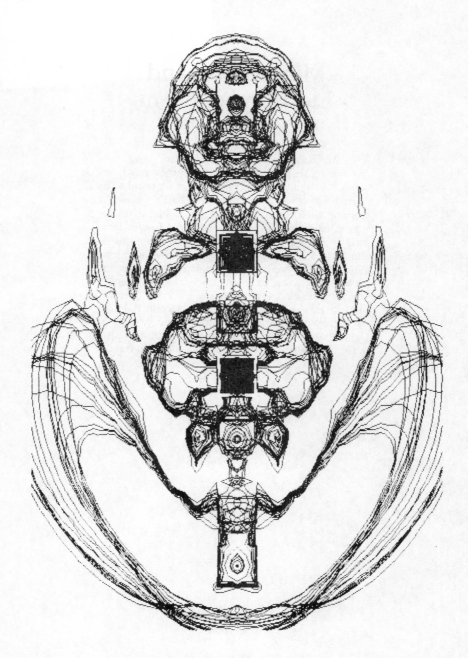

Wave patterns (chapter 8)

Mind, Body and Electromagnetism

John Evans

Element Books

© John Evans 1986
First published in Great Britain 1986 by
Element Books Ltd
Longmead, Shaftesbury, Dorset

British Library Cataloguing in Publication Data

Evans, John
Mind, body and electromagnetism.
1. Vertebrates—Physiology
I. Title
596'.01   QP31.2

ISBN 0 906540 86 0

Printed by
Billings, Hylton Road, Worcester

Contour pictures
by courtesy of Principia Mechanica, London

Text design by
Humphrey Stone

To my mother and father

Contents

Acknowledgements

I would like to thank all those who have taken an interest in this work over the years, and particularly my family who have waited so patiently for the book to be brought to a conclusion.

I am extremely grateful to those in orthodox academic fields for risking an interest; and I have much enjoyed the company of those who openly challenge current orthodoxy. I cannot honestly say which group were the more critical, or sympathetic. Not being deeply committed to either side, there was always the danger of pleasing no one, and not finding a publisher. However the work was not written to please, but to seek out some common ground. So my thanks to Ken Baily, Dr Sue Black, Professor Fred Burnham, Jean Byrom, Oliver Caldecott, Professor Dave Deamer and Jane, Penny Edwards, Dr Pieter Elliott, Jonathan Gavin, Olga Holbek, Robert and Eileen Ison, Dr Tidu Maini, Dr Joaquin Marti, Roger Newman Turner, Roy Ogden, Julian Pinfold, Mary Swithinbank, Dr Luca Turin, and Dr Gordon Woo.

I am indebted to Dr Adrian Fine and the editors of *The Lancet* for permission to reproduce the letter entitled *Back pain and acupuncture*; to the Basilius Press, Basel, for pictures from Hans Jenny's *Cymatics*; to the Manchester University Press for the use of H G Cannon's version of the four laws of Lamarck; and to Century Hutchinson for the quotations from Eileen Garrett.

Lastly, my thanks to Lisette Degioanni for the illustrations and to my son, John, for the design of the cover; and to Annie Walton and Michael Mann for guiding the production of the book.

Preface

I would suggest that the reader approaches this book as an adventure of ideas, and not as an academic text. There are several major themes, with exploratory variations, and the order of the material reflects my own developing thought over the years. In the earlier parts of the book, we consider possible ways of interpreting certain Eastern concepts in Western terms. Later, the exploration is more between the physical sciences and the life sciences, and with special reference to the part played by electromagnetism in the force fields of the body. Overall, we are concerned with the integration of knowledge.

I hope the reader will not be deterred by scientific technicalities, which I have tried to keep to an absolute minimum. Doubtless a few parts will be a little too mathematical for some, or too physiological for others. But much of it requires only an intelligent general interest in what is going on. Concerning any controversial evidence discussed, I take the view that prejudiced information is a natural hazard common to all our endeavours, whether termed scientific or otherwise, and it is therefore unwise to place too much emphasis on just one experimental aspect.

The prompting many years ago for embarking on this work was the sense that, in its extremes of specialisation and dogmatic assertion, and its denial of mental freedom, the pursuit of Western science was beginning to look a somewhat dangerous business – dangerous for the individual, and for society generally. Those who did not conform, who resisted the assumptions of behavioural psychology, who doubted the wisdom of certain new developments in medicine, who objected to particular technologies, were dissidents possibly in need of psychiatric treatment. Happily, this is not at all the situation today and, in many departments of knowledge, we seen an opening up to challenging influences from other cultures and older streams of thought.

Perhaps of most interest to scientifically-minded people will be the ideas about the growth of living forms in terms of low-frequency electromagnetics. In spite of all our new biochemical knowledge, the organisation of cells into a coherent whole remains a great mystery. Embryologists have talked vaguely about a controlling life-field, but not in any specific sense as would be appreciated by the physical scientist. Yet we have known for more than a hundred years that the varying nerve currents, which co-ordinate body activity, are inextricably linked with electromagnetic fields.

Today, some are using these forces in new therapies for cancer and bone growth. Others have begun the process of mapping and measuring the fields on the surface of the body, and categorising the rhythms and frequencies. In this book, we consider the possibility of a theoretical approach to these studies. As a minimum, I would hope to encourage others with more professional facilities for research than myself to pursue such lines of enquiry.

At the end of the last century, William James wrote that "when our science once becomes old fashioned, it will be more for its omissions of fact, its ignorance of whole ranges and orders of complexity in the phenomena to be explained, than for any fatal lack of its spirit and principles". As an introductory statement to this book, I doubt I could find anything more appropriate. Ignoring all the higher creative aspects of the conscious mind, many scientists are now devoted to the cause of reducing human activity to interactions of particles and genes. Within certain specialised disciplines, such constraints can have value. But as a general philosophical basis for understanding human nature, it becomes an irrational quest, and ultimately self-destructive. In any new-fashioning of our knowledge, we must surely try to restore a measure of commonsense and humanity.

John Evans
Cambridge
September 1985

Although he is keenly aware of light and colour in the world of which he is a part, man does not begin to recognise that he also participates in the brilliant pageantry of nature's ever-changing hues. This magnetic field in which he dwells can be likened to the shifting radiance of a rainbow. Unaware of being folded within this ever-changing film of colours, man covers his physical body with vivid clothes in order to gratify his own need for colour. He has this deep need, although he is far from understanding that in the true science of colour, every shade and tone has a particular effect upon the living organism.

Medicine has become more definitely aware of the therapeutic importance of colour in various forms of treatment, as it has also become more successful in the use of x-rays, infra-red and ultra-violet rays. But there still remains much to be discovered about the healing value of colour rays in the research and experiment of the future. When the unexplored possibilities of man's own radiation begin to unfold, a new comprehension of the nature and functioning of the human mind and consciousness will be formulated, and a wider use of the range of light and magnetic rays will be developed by Science.

Healing on a scale undreamed of as yet by medicine or psychology will soon be made possible, when further knowledge of the nature and strength of the rays contained within each body are charted and rightly directed. Then will it be more widely recognised that such fundamentally destructive states of negation, as doubt, fear and insecurity are at the root of man's physical ills. When at last he comes to understand that he himself gives out those vital rays which can either heal or destroy life, he will begin to accept his own responsibility, and he will desire to learn to direct and control his own radiations for the positive use of himself and his fellow men.

EILEEN GARRETT 1939

1. Changing Attitudes

During the course of this century, the disinterested search for knowledge on the part of a comparatively small number of dedicated people has been transformed into highly specialised investigations by a vast army of suitably disciplined researchers. In the process, the concept of science as the open-minded acquisition of knowledge has developed into something rather different. It has come to mean very particular ways of collecting evidence, and of conforming to a definite framework of laws and categories and assumptions, all of which considerably limit the fields of study. And with an aggressive attitude towards anything outside its prevailing monist-materialist philosophy, it has become a dubious social force, suppressing much that is of real human interest. Yet through the sheer scale and complexity of the research going on throughout the world, and the difficulties of absorption into some consensus viewpoint, science becomes more and more fragmented, and less able to develop general unifying concepts.

Now you may reasonably say that it is all too easy to criticise conventional science; but that it is only because of a measure of discipline and dogmatism that rational studies have got as far as they have. It is only by sticking rigidly to the quantitative and impersonal that we have been able to build up a body of knowledge that is generally valid for all observers on this earth. Without the constraints of repetitive experiment and mathematical formulation, we could so easily go off at a tangent, and perhaps find ourselves once again inventing unnecessary agencies to explain relatively simple phenomena. Instead of investigating, say, thunder and lightning in acoustical and electrical terms, we will recreate the demons and nature spirits. Surely modern science, for all its faults and limitations, has raised the minds of people to saner levels of thought. But yet, having rationalised and quantified natural phenomena in this way, the more thoughtful are left wondering if there is not very much more to things than this.

Fortunately, there is welcome evidence of more flexible attitudes. Many practising scientists would now agree that the disciplines imposed by the old physical laws, and the methods of collecting data in accordance with these laws, do not seem very helpful or even appropriate to the study of man himself. And maybe it is even causing some confusion in those areas that have always been the special preserve of physical science such as the atom and outer space. At both the human level in biochemistry and medicine, and at the extremes of the physical world in the very small, the very large, and the very fast, there are conceptual blockages that do not seem to allow for much further fundamental progress.

But there is nothing surprising about these blockages. Physical science has worked on the assumption of a physical world which is ordered and predictable, and so has sought out those things that appear reasonably ordered and predictable for special study. But our own thoughts, emotions, memories, and sense of identity are part of a conscious inner world whose characteristics are far from synonymous with those of physical space-time. Psychically, we interact with the physical universe, and yet are separate from it. In fact, this separateness is what allows us to study the physical aspects with such detachment.

The problem now for science is how to open out from the purely physical domain into that which is living and vital, conscious and intelligent. In doing this, we obviously do not wish to discard our detailed knowledge of atoms, molecules, and cells, but would like to incorporate this into something more general that involves the whole human experience. However, the present methods of science do not, and probably, by their very nature, cannot suggest a way forward from the physical to the psychical levels of everyday life, and it seems necessary to look elsewhere for solutions to our present difficulties.

To the hard-line materialist, this is quite pointless, for we are simply the product of our electrochemical activity. Apparently, the neuron circuitry of the brain requires no higher levels of control, becoming, once a certain level of complexity is reached, somehow aware of its own activity. It grows itself, it heals itself, it feels itself, it thinks itself, it wills itself, it develops rational and loving qualities. We are asked to believe that great art, and music, and literature, are just expressions of the nervous system; and that, prior to the present evolutionary stage, fantastically complex energy processes continued randomly for billions of years, unobserved by anything.

All of which is very hard to take, even for some of our brain specialists who are now postulating a 'world 2' and 'world 3' over and above the 'world 1' of physiology. Not that there is anything novel in this suggestion, for it is basic to almost all ancient and Eastern thought. The mind or ego, the astral body or soul, are the individualised projections of consciousness that ultimately determine the nature of physical experience. The mind is learning to control the physiology, and we are at the mercy of the genetic material very much to the extent that we choose to be. Although hidden from our limited physical senses, thought and feeling make us what we are; and as we evolve, we learn to free ourselves to some degree from the inherited constraints.

In Yoga philosophy, we have the explicit statement of the *causal body*, with the memory records of its own evolution, generating the *subtle body* of the mind and senses. In turn, this subtle body, or psyche, moulds the physical body into something reflecting its own nature. To the modern geneticist, this must be something of an over-statement. But as a minimum, the idea of a psychical-physical balance, and the conscious psyche slowly taking more and more control over internal organic processes, is surely a very reasonable evolutionary viewpoint.

However, there is a vast difference between the vague subjective Western use of the term 'psyche' (which to some psychologists has no validity at all), and the objective Eastern descriptions of the subtle body, involving seven principal oscillatory vortices from the base of the spine to the cerebral cortex, and generally corresponding in position and function to what has been learnt this century about the main hormone centres. Roughly speaking, the trunk centres may be said to constitute the subconscious psyche, and the cerebral centres to reflect all aspects of mind. Different perceptual states such as in dreams, hypnosis, and out-of-body experience represent selective stimulation of these centres, and with suitable training, can be produced almost to order. Thus, with this 'modular' understanding of psychical organisation, there is no inherent difficulty in conceptualising together both normal and abnormal psychical experience.

Control of the physical body is effected through certain mediating levels of force which, in most Western esoteric schools of thought, constitute the etheric or bioplasmic energy body. This is the structural system linking physical and psychical, and containing the vital energies of *prana* or *Qi* that control the overall development of cellular material. Psychically, this may be considered as the deepest unconscious level, involving all the autonomic processes over which we have the least conscious control.

To some, such ideas make immediate sense, perfectly complementing physical ideas; to others, they are complete anathema, introducing unnecessary mystical elements. Naturally, the one-world or monist view must maintain that a total explanation of human life will be found through a sufficiently detailed understanding of physical energy, and the concept of separate structural and psychical entities can have no obvious usefulness. With this view, ideas about such matters as free will, mental healing, past lives, and projection from the body, must be a nonsense, and this has to be the materialist position. But with the more pragmatic concepts of a multi-system or pluralist organisation, the possibilities and potentialities for human experience and development take on quite new dimensions.

In the East, esoteric knowledge has been forbidden to all except a very privileged few considered worthy to enter into higher mental and spiritual development. Western people suspect this secrecy, and see elements of selfishness in such privilege. But whether the reasons for keeping this knowledge secret are valid or not, it has been circulating relatively openly for the past hundred years, albeit in some rather specialised literature. The only reason it can now be said to be 'hidden' to Western people is that those who have studied it have been unable to find an acceptable way of presenting it to the formal schools of thought and disciplines of academic life.

So whatever arguments did exist for secrecy now seem to have been overtaken by events, and there seems no good reason for not bringing it to the clear light of day, especially if it has relevance to modern conceptual problems. And it is certainly of interest and significance that some of the more open-minded practitioners of science and medicine are turning towards Eastern ideas, or suggesting alternative approaches that have much in common with esoteric thought.

This is in no way surprising. Western science, coming through certain Greek and Christian traditions, has worked largely on the external world and all that seemed relatively independent of the mind. Esoteric ideas, coming from Indian, Platonic, and artistic sources, concentrate on man's inner energies and structures, together with the development of mental processes that suggest new possibilities for human evolution. Sooner or later, these two branches must meet – as perhaps they once did in the Pythagorean schools, and as they do to some extent in Chinese philosophy. When we are able to surmount the language barriers, they should together create something much more comprehensive, while giving point and purpose to some of our barren quantitative knowledge.

Materialist thinking goes back to the Greek philosophers Leucippus and Democritus who postulated that all matter was composed of indivisible and indestructible atoms. By contrast, Plato thought of atoms in much less concrete terms. Different types were characterised by different shapes; and through geometrical transformations, they could change from one type into another. After the famous Copenhagen Conference in 1926 when the philosophical implications of quantum and wave mechanics were thoroughly discussed, physics seemed to move away from materialism towards Platonic thought-forms. Atoms and subatomic particles could no longer be precisely defined in terms of the motions of specific points, there being an inevitable degree of uncertainty about all space-time parameters. They had wave as well as corpuscular characteristics, and could be transformed into other types of particles. Werner Heisenberg, who played such a major part in bringing about a change of attitude, talks of a tendency, a potentiality, a probability for atomic events to take place, in contrast to the previous certainties of classical physics.

The idea of a 'fundamental' particle is not a very plausible concept. Everything in the physical world, however small, would seem to possess both form and vibration. In Buddhism, there is a primordial space-energy (*akasa*), and the particles of matter are conceived as particular vortex forms of this energy. Thus matter is not considered as in any real sense different from the energy that flows through, and constitutes space. In Western science one recognises this type of thinking in classical electromagnetics, or in the concept of gravitational stress as a geometrical distortion of space-time. Along such lines, it seems more plausible to consider an elementary particle as a specially concentrated field of energy, with characteristic vibrations that determine its interaction with the immediate environment.

Today, it would be difficult to place physics in any neat philosophical category. In the high-energy, high-frequency experimental work with particle accelerators, the billiard-ball approach seems to have taken over completely. But in the conceptual work, the introduction of reverse-time and imaginary events has added an intriguing mystical element. However, regardless of philosophy, what is now apparent to all is that, through the fission of heavy elements, or the fusion of light elements, some of the mass-energy concentrated in atomic vortices can be released to generate those cosmic or spatial energies in which we are all immersed. Thus East and West can agree that we form part of an energy complex of infinite diversity where the energies of space merge into the energies of matter; and in our own bodies, there is a gradation from the most subtle low-frequency electromagnetic vibrations to the gigantic protein molecules containing many thousands of atomic units. This type of energy conceptualisation is a powerful and unifying view, helping us to see ourselves, not as lonely individuals whiling away the time on a deserted space-ship called earth, but as receptors of the cosmic energies from the furthermost points of space at every moment of time. Some of this energy we see directly; other energy we experience indirectly; and with much of it we have as yet no means of knowing what its effects are.

Our physical perceptions, then, give us a very partial view of what

is going on. They force us to concentrate on material energy by selecting those energies that show up matter through reflection. If we did
not select these electromagnetic light rays, but say, selected radiation
that passed through matter, we would not be aware, visually, of the
existence of the physical world. Presumably there are good reasons
for this screening of eye and brain. It may be that we would be unable
to cope with any more. It may be that we have definite tasks to
perform in the physical world, and so must have our attention clearly
focussed on the material. It may be that only physical experience
can develop certain mental and emotional qualities. Or it may be that
our current level of perception simply indicates our evolutionary
position.

Through the new systems work, with modular structures hier-
archically organised, we are gradually acquiring a new language for
discussing these complex energy problems. In particular, the relation
of hardware circuitry to the programmed software has opened up
some new thought-forms that look like being helpful and useful. For
instance, the separable, but interactive nature of mind and body may
have parallels with the concept of software as an entity existing in its
own right, and yet able to control many different machines. It would
be unwise to take such analogies too literally: computers do, regardless of modern mythology, precisely what the programmer directs.
However, anything that can be standardised or systematised can be
simulated on a machine; and the idea is growing that, for the more
routine aspects of behaviour at least, there are in-built procedural
entities for controlling the specialised motor neuron networks.

Whether these controls take the form of some molecular or genetic
coding, or are part of separate energy systems, or both, is probably
impossible to determine by detailed physical observation. Just given a
small computer with a few thousand instructions, there is no way we
can begin to understand what is going on without general design
knowledge. And with about ten billion neurons in the brain, each
with millions of complex molecules, we would be wasting our time
with microscopic electrochemical methods. We first have to get the
right feel for the overall organisation – and this means a careful study
of all psychical and psychosomatic evidence without prior prejudice
about what is possible. In modern systems work, this is the only
rational approach open in the circumstances of almost total ignorance. Without the broad outline of how a system is put together, and
some understanding of the highest levels of control, it is so easy to get
bogged down in all the minute detail – as most researchers now are.

It is surely the failure to work from the psychical level that has led
medical science into many cul-de-sacs, so that it has to classify vari-

ous conditions as incurable. This has even resulted in imprisonment for some who dared to claim otherwise. Orthodox practitioners continue to treat the most obvious physical symptoms, seldom inquiring into the deeper sources of trouble. Yet we learn every day from systems work that the apparent effects of breakdown are often far removed from the real problems, and treating them in isolation can lead to a much worse situation. Only comparatively recently has medicine begun to reconsider the rather obvious idea that much illness is related to stress and strain, and that such matters require positive thought instead of drugs and surgery which are in themselves inherently damaging.

In transplant surgery, we have the ultimate culmination of the mechanical-materialist approach. Just how many come to the point of transplant through previous physical therapies, we will never be told; and just how desparate things can become for the failures, we will never truly appreciate. Even when the surgery is adjudged to be successful, powerful drugs must then be indefinitely administered to prevent rejection by the immunological system. To those in natural therapeutics, these are seriously misguided procedures – quite apart from the separate issue of removing organs from a dying person. One must work with the natural forces which are there for our protection and regeneration; and by allowing the physical symptoms to act as positive indicators of what to do, we can assist the subconscious controls to overcome energy imbalance and obstruction.

So much can in fact be done from the psychical level alone. By opening up direct channels of communication to the subconscious memory and autonomic forces, and making appropriate suggestion, what might appear a miracle to the biblical mind can sometimes occur. Curing blindness, creating new bone material, eliminating cancerous growth, and adapting to serious brain damage, have all been achieved through suitably directed mental energy.

The engineering approach to medical problems is also encouraged by certain 'spiritual' attitudes which stress the essential separateness of body and soul – and caricatured by the little man sitting on top of the pineal gland. Thus the physical body can be treated in a purely mechanistic way without disturbing the soul; while animals, having no soul, can be experimented on without concern for individual feeling. This is not a very tenable or ethical viewpoint, and many theologians have now given up the concept of soul altogether, inclining towards a materialist position, and leaving God to fill in the problem areas. All of which makes for immense complications in their attempt to understand human experience, or even to explain the thoughts and actions of the founder of their faith.

The attraction of monism, whether scientific or theological, is the idea of the essential unity and simplicity of everything, which appeals to a certain aesthetic sense. The physicists, searching for a primary particle of matter, or for a unified energy theory, have tried extremely hard to work out this monism in the physical universe. But with new particles being postulated all the time, artificial 'laws' continually being invoked about this or that energy category, and causal relationships having to be held together by 'virtual' and 'imaginary' phenomena, the basic theoretical edifice begins to look very doubtful indeed. By contrast, the dualism of the inter-related Yin and Yang, physical and etheric, appears most elegant; and in its more detailed or pluralistic forms involving many intermediate categories of action, it seems to embrace so much more of the phenomenal and living world. There is, to paraphrase William James, such a 'thinness' about monism, with apparently nothing in between particle energies and the highest transcendental experience.

But it is the monist approach to evidence that is the major problem. Here one sometimes finds definite pre-electromagnetic, pre-Maxwell attitudes, with a quite inexplicable failure to take into account just how extremely selective and constrained our visual systems are. Those who claim to see a little more of the environmental energies than normal are likely to be considered in need of some psychiatric treatment. Yet as everyone should now be aware, our eyes are receptive only to a single octave of the eighty or so octaves of electromagnetic radiation. We cannot see radio waves, ultra-violet light, and x-rays; we cannot see the earth's gravitational and magnetic fields or the enveloping radiation bands; we cannot see our own internal structure, or the interior of the earth. Whatever its faults, conventional science has considerably expanded our limited physical perception by means of instrumentation capable of detecting and analysing energies outside the human perceptual range. The point has now been reached where it requires very little imagination to conceive of a variety of perceptual states that extend physical perception.

Those who suddenly find themselves in curious trance states, such as are likely to occur with spinal injuries and hospital anaesthetics, often comment on their ability to see much that was formerly invisible, followed by a certain sadness on returning to normal consciousness with its limited view of the world and human energies. Such experiences may not be essentially different from everyday life, in that material forms take on their usual appearance. But much more is observed, such as the delicate vibrations surrounding living organisms, or the coloured radiations associated with cerebral activity. It would seem that some unusual states of perception simply indicate an extra sensitivity towards force fields and energy flows that we have some inkling of, but which can only be discerned indirectly through specialised instrumentation, or conceptualised in terms of complex mathematical formulations.

Even more challenging (because of their repeatability) to materialist assumptions are the various phenomena associated with hypnosis. The movement 'through time', the rigidity of the body in the cataleptic state, the control of one mind over another, the transfer of thought and sensation, the changes in visual perception and notions of reality through simple suggestion – these are all matters well researched, and well beyond the scope of physical rationalisation.

Probably of most interest today is the access through hypnosis to the full, but largely unconscious, memory of all past experience, and involving not only emotional and objective content, but pre-life material as well. As there is no evidence to connect these far-memories with the genetic material of relatives, those who reject the past-life interpretation would have to assume that memory recall suddenly aberrates at the point of birth from a truthful process to something purely imaginative – and this does not accord with the historical facts that can be checked. There are even a few Western people who have direct conscious access to some of this material.

Memory has always been an immense problem for the scientist, and the search for the memory engram, in terms of brain circuitry, or RNA, or neurotransmitters, has produced nothing. In fact, modern evidence from brain surgery strongly suggests that the function of the brain core, and the hippocampus in particular, concerns not the memories themselves, but conscious access to memory. And the evidence from hypnosis indicates that the whole of experience, both internal and external vibrational patterns, is channelled by the sensing systems through to some relatively indestructible psychical form. This unique memory-stream is the basis of all human activity, and the source of our individuality.

This type of evidence can be absorbed without essential difficulty into a pluralistic view, but not into a materialist one. In fact, with the latter, we can hardly make an intelligent start on any human cerebral activity except the most automated. Even if we could appreciate all the connections between the billions of neurons, we would still be left with the basic problem of how any specific train of impulses is consciously initiated. Taken to its logical conclusion, everything must be of the nature of a conditioned reflex, with no room for rational analysis and the ability to choose. This would also apply to the research questions being postulated; and one would have to assume that all potential answers were preprogrammed. If we do not have individual choice in the search for knowledge, or truth, or conceptual consistency, then the idea of rational scientific investigation becomes completely meaningless. And for scientists to express the typical materialist conclusions that deny the validity of the conscious processes leading to the conclusions, this is surely the ultimate *reductio ad absurdum*.

Nevertheless, orthodox science must continue to reject much that is of interest, regardless of the evidence. But such continuous rejection eventually loses all credibility, and we begin to wonder if there is something inherent in physical perception that gives not only a restricted view in terms of frequency or range, but a definite one-sided asymmetrical appearance. At all levels of study there are suggestions of missing complementary entities, even dimensions. The atom, for instance, is electrically asymmetrical, with so many of its properties seemingly based on the negative electron. All living organic molecules exist only in one specifically polarised 'right' or 'left' form. The (3–1) continuum is dimensionally asymmetrical with regard to space and time. Matter is gravitationally asymmetrical, with material sinks but no sources. And the outward physical energies of the whole universe as perceived by scientific instrumentation disappear into the infinite.

Through the consideration of various perception states, and the related problems of energy, space, and time, we move forward to a radically different view of the universe and ourselves. Through physical-etheric interaction and complementary Yin-Yang processes, we take a new look at all the problems of material structure, growth, repair, and overall cohesion and unity. We attempt to grasp how the external experience of space may give rise to the internal experience of time. We look at the inward gravitational, and outward electromagnetic and particle flows of the sun in terms of a balanced oscillatory process, in which the entropy, or potential for disorder of the physical energies, is counteracted by the inward formative forces. We perceive a world in which all electromagnetic radiation is experienced directly in terms of colour. And within all this, we are able to conceive the human processes, not in the hard physical outline of materialism, but as inextricably related to the environmental energies – with cosmic forces affecting us, and we in turn helping to create or destroy the cosmos through our own mental and emotional patterns.

With just a few simple ideas about energy transformations leading to extended-physical, or reverse-physical states of perception, we can move on without irrationality to the non-physical worlds of the mystics, or the alternative states of experience of those with unusual psychical abilities. Not that we have to accept all they say, because it would seem more or less impossible to avoid personal bias in states where individual thought and feeling have direct effects on the environment. But it is surely a most natural idea that that which gives life to material forms, and that which we call mental and emotional – all, in fact, that is most real to us – might be experienced more objectively in some other perception state, with or without the physical systems.

A basic task in science now is not so much to define what things are in some absolute sense, but what perception states are possible, and how one state relates to another in terms of energy activity. In its present form, science is a one-sided perceptual study; and with it goes the obvious danger of drawing general conclusions from instrumental observation of suitably selected phenomena. Not perceiving the mental and emotional processes, we try to explain everything in mechanistic terms. Physical life is an extremely testing experience, requiring deep thought and challenging situations for us to begin to conceive the possibility of a broader framework in which our limited senses function. However, presumably alternative perceptions may also be one-sided; and those who renounce the world and discount physical knowledge completely, do not obviously acquire any monopoly of wisdom and understanding.

There must be a degree of subjectivity in all perceptual states. But whether sane or insane, conscious or subconscious, in the body or out of it, there is presumably some meaning to all that we perceive. At one extreme for instance, Parkinsonian patients, often intelligent and articulate people, have provided us with wonderful descriptions of the gyrations and distortions of space-time energies as they pass in and out of various perceptual states under the influence of the drug l-Dopa. Their space is different from our space, being one in which they directly observe the colours and vibrations of their own thought-forms. At another extreme, adepts apparently observe the solar system, not in the two-dimensional ecliptic plane, but three-dimensionally in lotus form, with the sun at the end of a long tube of energy. Thirty years ago, this could only have been considered a form of insanity; but as our simple particle pictures of the solar system are gradually replaced by the complex dynamics of swirling magnetic fields and cosmic particles, we begin to hesitate to say who has the more realistic view.

Radically new investigations into the nature of living systems are now developing. At the psychical and perceptual levels, there is the objective testing of memory regression, remote viewing, and the visualisation of low-frequency fields not normally seen. In psychosomatics, we are beginning to realise the possibilities for conscious control of the autonomic processes through mental imaging. At the structural level, new field and frequency concepts are emerging. In physiology, there is a range of experimentation into the electromagnetism of the body, and the effects of low-frequency energy on various structures. Some of this is a return to nineteenth century work, but we return with more detailed physical knowledge, a more subtle technology, and an appreciation of the significance of certain Eastern concepts of human structure and function. Slowly the whole mind-body question is being opened up once again. From both a conceptual and experimental viewpoint, there are signs of a new stage in the evolution of rational thought.

Many of the new studies are inter-disciplinary, and not specialised like the present departments of science. Work on perceptual matters, for instance, requires a range of ideas from physics, chemistry, physiology, medicine, and psychology, quite apart from any contributions Eastern ideas can make. But it is definitely not statistically-orientated. Statistics takes over when the ideas run out, or when the causal chains are too difficult to follow, or when we have reached the limits of observation. In psychical matters especially, statistics deadens constructive thought and experiment; and to be told that *psi* phenomena must be valid because of certain odds against, impresses very few, least of all the mathematician. Eileen Garrett who tried so hard to get scientists interested in alternative perceptual states, and who helped to found the schools of para-psychology, soon found herself up against the statistical method, and so was largely thwarted in what she set out to do. Sadly this tradition has continued in parapsychology, and little or no progress has been made in developing causal ideas.

This century has been a time for detailed analysis rather than synthesis. Slowly the various specialisations have separated out, and then tended to develop in relative isolation from other branches of thought. So today there are many scientists who, having given their whole lives to the working out of a particular physical concept, are finding great difficulty in understanding just what is going on. They feel threatened by the changing and sometimes hostile attitudes, fearing that we may be regressing into primitive and irrational modes of thought. They are even attacking the founder of their faith, Sir Isaac Newton, apparently implying that while writing the *Principia*, he was mentally deranged through mercury poisoning. Newton's esoteric interests have always been something of an embarrassment – as also is the psychical research of the magnanimous Alfred Russell Wallace who postulated the general form of the Theory of Evolution before his friend Darwin. The specialist mind can never comprehend the original mind.

Thoughts and ideas are living things that compete for survival; and if the present philosophical mode of science leads to conclusions that cannot be said to be either reasonable or rational, then it must develop on a different basis. If, for example, man is considered to be just a biochemical process resulting from random mutations, then it is irrational to think that the individual self can in any way be responsible for his actions, let alone analyse his own structure. Materialism surely represents a specialised form of observation and analysis rather than any coherent philosophy on which we can base our judgements. With a suitably restrictive outlook concerning the space-time appearance of things, concepts of free will and responsibility have no apparent meaning. But when faced with the conscious decisions and experiences of everyday life, we find that such simplistic ideas just collapse.

One would hope that the new understandings of physical and psychical structure will have a significant impact in the redirection of psychological studies. At one end of the scale, there are the cosmic generalisations of Jung which, in the light of regression studies, appear only as partial truths. At the other end, there are the behaviourists who admit only the existence of conditioned reflexes in the nervous system, and therefore cannot logically distinguish human and animal behaviour. All the orthodox schools indulge in gross over-simplification of types, and tend to conceptualise any sort of dissident behaviour as some form of neurotic complex. Thus, our modern psychologists have paved the way for the abuses to be found in totalitarian states, whether of the right or left. There, individuality must be strictly held in check by social conformity, regardless of the magnitude of the issues. Not that this ruthlessness is the prerogative of governments, for through ridicule and ostracism, the scientific and medical hierarchies enforce their own brand of conformity. By comparison, dogmatic theology, and the hypnotic methods of ritual and ceremony, now appear rather mild and tolerant.

However incredible the medieval systems of psychology appear to the modern mind, they do at least begin from the assumption that each individual is unique in his development and in his future potential. This is also what the exploration of memory under hypnosis makes clear to us – the subconscious records constituting for each person an individual stream of consciousness. Behind every decision and action, there is this vast panorama of experience that motivates and guides. Our evolution is all there to be read, but naive psychology refuses even to open the book. We have lost the keys to the ancient psychologies, thus either dismissing them, or contenting ourselves with mechanistic procedures that have come down to us. Now that we have almost reached the point of self-destruction, this is surely the time for the most radical change of approach.

The personal problem for the scientist today lies in the fact that he has to exist in two quite separate worlds which he has no way of reconciling. He conceives his scientific endeavours and abstract theorising to be his rational side – which is basically separate from his everyday life and natural dealings with other people. Just how his knowledge of genes or DNA relates to normal thought and conversation, he has no idea. Certain psychologists of the behavioural school even go so far as to deny thought as an independent activity, thus rather delightfully confusing us all every time they give an opinion on anything. But as we delve more deeply into the psychosomatics, into memory and subconscious motivations, we begin to realise that what the scientist may consider to be his rational scientific self may in fact be an expression of emotional attitudes, or of irrational blockages, arising from a variety of conditions in past experience. This may apply to people in all walks of life, including the theologian who, apparently arguing from deep conviction, is instinctively reacting to a particularly difficult experience that is largely hidden from the conscious mind.

Whether the fashionable attitudes of orthodox science today are more determined by rationality or prejudice is difficult to say. But it is important that we at least take into account psychological aspects. And it is important that we try to find concepts and ideas that bridge the gap of the two cultures that we are creating through scientific and non-scientific activity. In the first instance, as indicated in this book, we may have to release ourselves from some of the highly meticulous attitudes of the separate specialisations in order to grasp the broader picture. But if this leads to a position where we can truly say that our scientific studies are at one with our human studies, that the scientific dynamics of living things are as we directly perceive them to be, and emotionally feel them to be, then for our own psychical balance this is surely all to the good.

The principal implication of the new studies and attitudes is the realisation that the world, and how we choose to spend our time in it, will be more and more determined by our thought and will, thus hopefully encouraging us to higher levels of rationality. But at the same time, we are coming to understand that, in the exclusive development of the rational side, we may lose our sanity and humanity, even our common sense. A more balanced approach is required involving all our psychical potential. In this, there may be some sense of an 'expanded consciousness', although quite different in character from that of some of our modern cults in their retreat from reason, and the cultivation of aggressive new dogmas. Nor has it any connection with the fashionable new academic esotericism which suggests that knowledge and enlightenment must necessarily be in terms of some unintelligible mysticism.

During the course of the century, the Western scientific mind has more and more been coming to the conclusion that either the psychical side does not exist in its own right, or it belongs to some non-rational category completely outside any causal or structural order. If there is to be any 'new awareness', it is first and foremost a reversal of these trends – through a conscious recognition of our deeper memory structures, and of the conceptual freedom of the mind, without which it would be absolutely impossible to discuss these matters.

Unfortunately, once the conscious mind has been caught up in some orthodox consensus of thought, it becomes extremely resistant to change. All strong dogmatic belief, particularly if inculcated early in life, is to some extent self-fulfilling; and at a certain mental level, it would seem that truth and belief are largely synonymous.

In the life-sciences, orthodox research involves the seeking out of standardised structural, functional, and behavioural features, thus looking all the time for the lowest common denominators of life. With the animal kingdom, where there would seem to be comparatively little individuality, this may be the natural thing to do; but then to extrapolate from animal to man, as so often happens in medical science, is likely to lead to serious error. Unlike an animal species, we are characterised by our differences – we look different, we behave differently, we have vastly different abilities, and we react quite differently to mental and physical stimuli. All natural experience accentuates our differences, regardless of the levelling-down tendency of most social institutions, and their encouragement to some common moulding of attitude and behaviour.

It is not at all surprising that, as our science grows more institutionalised, it tries to dictate to its members what phenomena may be considered valid, and what are mental aberrations of the individual. In this way, it is possible to miss everything that is ultimately interesting. Human consciousness and mentality are too subtle for the molecular and cellular methods of biological science, or for the primitive categories of behavioural psychology. In the West, these are explored through the separate culture of literature and the arts.

If we are to understand ourselves at the rational conscious level, then the source of individuality arising from the unique memory-stream of experience must be clearly recognised. The science that first reduces us to species level, and then to neural mechanisms, is a deadening influence, seriously threatening both our individual development, and the evolution of science itself. The concept of individual uniqueness has to be fought for, not only in the political and religious context, but above all in the quest for knowledge and understanding.

There is nothing static about the human organism. In all rationalisations, the capacity for change and evolution must be taken into account. What may have been generally true a few thousand years ago, may be specifically untrue about certain human beings today. Undoubtedly a few people are born with, or acquire, most unusual powers that are well outside the norm for society. To a few adepts, it would seem that disease is no longer a problem because the necessary controls at the mental level have been established over the autonomic functions of the body. Man becomes less at the mercy of primitive emotional forces, and inherited genetic tendencies. Medicine and biochemistry are shifting forms of knowledge, and disease and illness are functions of evolution. Most of us are in some intermediate stage of development where our conscious mind has only limited understanding of lower levels, thus resulting in an inability to cope with many expressions of energy imbalance.

It is as well also to remember that we do to some extent create our own version of reality, whether about the unseen quarks and gluons of the physicist, or simply our view of other people. The way things currently appear to be is conditioned by the thoughts of previous generations, and the education we receive about these thoughts. Under hypnosis, the mental automaton will accept almost any suggestion, however bizarre, and completely reverse normal conscious attitudes and patterns of behaviour if so instructed.

But at the highest psychical level, we are developing a conceptual freedom to perceive things in a larger context, and also the will to influence significantly the way things will evolve. Our human studies, therefore, can never be a clear-cut mathematical science like electromagnetic physics, and should never aspire to be. The cohesive energies of life are continuously creative; and if we are to acquire meaningful knowledge of them, this must be kept firmly in mind.

2. Special Insights

Let us now consider in a little more depth certain less restrictive viewpoints briefly referred to, together with some associated psychical research. Eastern esotericism, taking us beyond the material and mechanical into pluralist and multi-system concepts, provides an intelligible psychology of normal experience as well as giving plausible rationalisations of unusual psychical phenomena. Not that this means it is true; but at least we begin from a basis that does not contradict a certain intuitive sense, and does not automatically exclude great areas of human existence.

The Eastern mystics who follow the world-renouncing paths of meditation towards an ultimate enlightenment have been intensely secretive of their knowledge, having an intrinsic belief that the divine secrets of life must not be placed before the cynical and primitive thought-forms of those who have not aspired to higher life. But a number of Western people have tried to enter into the spirit of this Eastern wisdom; and, through the early theosophists in particular, there now exists a most interesting body of literature that makes certain Indian concepts at least partially intelligible to a Western audience. The highly respected Alfred Sinnett, for example, once the editor of *The Indian Times*, had a significant impact on the English-speaking world with his book *Esoteric Buddhism* published just over a century ago. At the beginning of this century, we have the German writings and lectures of Dr Rudolf Steiner that attempt to deal with almost every aspect of knowledge, and his ideas have flowed out into social, educational, medical, agricultural, and artistic fields, as well as the abstractions of science and philosophy. Steiner's *anthroposophy* adds a Christian dimension to the Buddhist's spiritual atheism. And with suggestions of energy-holes and negative mass, it has quite a modern ring to it. A more recent exponent of these philosophical trends, Paul Brunton, has written informatively of his initiation into the Eastern psychologies, and the problems of their translation into Western ways and thought.

The Victorians were well prepared for these more pluralistic philosophies in which subtle distinctions were made between various aspects of mind, and soul, and spirit. There had been immense interest in unusual psychical phenomena from the beginning of the century, much of it deriving from the curious work of Franz Mesmer – once a most respected conventional doctor, but who later discarded orthodox therapy in favour of hypnotic and magnetic methods. Given the right sort of cases, he made the blind to see and the lame to walk. But his miraculous cures were inevitably dismissed by contemporary medical theorists. However, it led in time to new ideas about the subconscious and psychosomatics, to detailed investigations of sleep-walking states, to the exploration of long-term memory, and many other psychical studies.

Also developing along somewhat similar lines during the century were the spiritualist investigations into discarnate intelligence. They also used trance states, and were deeply interested in the energy fields and vibrations of the body. The great and good Alfred Russell Wallace, who with Charles Darwin propounded the Theory of Evolution, was one of these; and unlike today, it seems not to have caused his scientific colleagues, even Huxley, any embarrassment. Wallace became an untiring advocate both for evolutionary theory, and for the validity of spiritualist communication.

During this more materialist century, psychical research has had much less impact, in spite of the efforts of the one-time spiritualist, Eileen Garrett, in founding the schools of parapsychology. And there has been comparatively little development in hypnosis, either in basic understanding or in therapeutic use. Reading the *Principles of Psychology* of William James, written before the turn of the century, one is inclined to conclude that rather less than more is known about this state. In this field, the one really impressive person this century is Edgar Cayce who has left us with the results of forty years of almost daily investigation – mainly of a medical nature, but also giving new insight into older philosophies.

Looking first at these older philosophies, the idea perhaps most fundamental to them is that what appears to us as the physical space-time world is just part of, a projection of, a much greater reality involving other energy and perceptual domains. This in fact would be in general accord with the latest theories from mathematical-physics in which every point of space-time represents a hidden multiple-dimensional structure. We are told that through certain forms of mental discipline, it is possible to bypass the normal constraints of eye and brain inherent in physical perception, becoming aware for instance of the more subtle processes of the psyche that influence the physical aspects. In doing this, we do not necessarily lose our awareness of individual identity with all the normal flow of thought and feeling, but rather expand our experience through heightened forms of perception that give new insights. Physical perception then, according to this view, is a particular and limiting experience, enabling us to sort out matter in most of its forms through the emission and reflection of light rays. Non-physical perception implies a direct sensing of other forms of energy that are not filtered in this way by the cerebral systems, and may involve such characteristics as reverse-time or timelessness.

Within this overall view of the cosmos, man has a complex multi-system structure, with atomic matter of the physical body representing the lowest aspect in the control hierarchy. Immediately above this is the etheric system, or body of vital forces, or lifebody, which all plant and animal life are said to possess, and which in man forms the link between the material body and the higher systems of the psyche. The etheric is the basic control and organisational system for the molecular and cellular organism, and transmits from the higher systems the essential life-forming and healing powers for the physical. Disease and illness we are told result from physical-etheric imbalance, and most of natural therapeutics is based on such an idea. The etheric is sometimes referred to as the double-body in that it is supposed to duplicate, or precisely complement, the structure of the physical body.

Steiner describes the etheric system in terms of streams of forces that have built up the physical body; and also as a form of light permeating the body, extending just beyond the physical boundary. He discusses blood circulation and the heart in these terms, stating that the blood is continuously changing between material and etherised states – not a surprising statement in view of the fact that we generate about two million new blood cells each second. Its circulation is essentially energised by localised etheric or autonomic forces, leaving the heart more akin to a dam than a pump.

In fact, the concept of an organising field working locally rather than from a centralised source is fairly basic to this type of thinking. Thus, for instance, when we cut our hand, or have a tooth removed, the local biofield remains, and immediately begins its work of re-organising the surrounding structures. Materialist science has as yet no understanding of the structural and geometrical aspects of healing, but is well aware of certain curious phenomena pointing towards a biofield approach. If, for instance, tissue is taken from one part of certain small creatures and packed into another area where a leg is missing, then a normal limb may be regenerated. Also the strange matter of phantom-limb pain is naturally explained along these lines.

The etheric or bioplasmic viewpoint is much associated with hypnosis, and with various skin conditions amenable to such methods.

We are told by clairvoyant observation of a falling away, or realignment, of the cerebral fields under hypnosis, allowing special access to the subconscious mind and the autonomics of the body. It is argued that abnormal skin conditions indicate some physical or psychical problem preventing the etheric system from working naturally on the body; and through suitable hypnotic activation of cerebral centres, a bioplasmic reorganisation can take place having almost immediate normalising effects on the skin. Alternatively, the reverse can happen, with blisters and burns quickly appearing through harmful hypnotic suggestion.

Higher in the control hierarchy are the feeling and thinking systems of the astral and ego. The astral, or lower soul, we share in common with the animal world; but in man, the ego, the 'I', the sense of separate identity, is slowly transforming the more primitive astral functions. In fact, this process is said to be the main characteristic of the Piscean or Christian age, involving more conscious control over the emotional life, and the development of aesthetic sensitivity. In further developments in the coming eras, man will slowly learn to direct the autonomic systems within the body, eventually even to the point of having direct control of physical structuring. Anatomically, these developments are linked to the major control centres of the brain, especially the pituitary and hypothalamus.

However, as we are more drawn into physical existence, and with individual identity and independence strengthened, man is tending to cut himself off from the source of life. This descent into matter, and the sense of separation it creates, is considered to be at the root of most of our psychological problems. Thus part of our development must be to find a way back to our origins. Through deep meditation, through mental control of the body and the emotions, Steiner maintained that we can *objectively* investigate the non-physical domains, and come to new understandings of the unseen psychical processes that work continuously within our human systems.

He, like other mystics, was quite sure that such abilities were an intrinsic part of man's consciousness in earlier times, and gave certain civilisations specific powers which seem so mysterious today. Now, with our perceptions embedded in the physical, we have largely lost our ability to perceive the broader framework of the cosmos. So we are left with the one-sided investigations of modern science that can make little sense of anything that lives and grows, and only feels on safe ground when dealing with comparatively static and inert material forms.

The main scientific interest in these ideas is the possible existence of biofields – either reflecting or regulating electrochemical activity. If esoteric concepts are valid, the field would have a number of distinctive components, including a structural field relating to cellular organisation, and various psychical fields involving sexual, emotional, mental, and spiritual development. Most descriptions of the biofield aura indicate a triple energy envelope of the body. There is an inner health aura following the body contours that is fairly static; and where there is disease or disorder, a certain darkening and distortion is observed. Surrounding this are emotional and mental fields providing a brilliant display of form and colour reflecting the changing patterns of psychical activity.

Many Victorians took the view that the field was magnetic in nature. In their experiments with sleep-walkers and mediums, they noted that the aural fields of magnets as described by trance subjects were in accord with scientific concepts, and also gave the impression of directly affecting the human biofields. During this century, there have been extensive biofield studies by Dr Harold Burr of Yale University, who showed that all living entities possess an electrical life-field intimately associated with physical development, and responding to more cosmic influences.

Some researchers have recently been claiming to photograph the aura by means of Kirlian photography, pioneered by the Russian scientist Semyon Kirlian and his wife Valentina. This is a high-voltage, high-frequency electrical process which often gives inner and outer aural effects, sometimes suggestive of mental and emotional states. In medical science, the heat aura is now being used in diagnostic work and there are various other imaging processes reflecting different aspects of the electromagnetics of the body. However, through hypnosis, it would seem that we all have the latent ability to view these biofields directly, and more and more people are developing Yoga and other methods for doing this. Some, like Eileen Garrett, had this ability from childhood; and in her adult descriptions, in her book *My Life as a Search for the Meaning of Mediumship*, there is a certain beauty and authority.

The movement of this energy is not visible to ordinary sight. In my own case I first see movement in colour and light; the nature of this primary action taking place throughout space is a rotating one; and out of it are born all my objective clairvoyant perceptions. I am aware of heavy inchoate darkness, before I begin to see form clairvoyantly. This darkness is charged with pulsing, breathing, movement which bursts into curving rays of light and colour. Some of these seem to split from the original parent rays, and moving out, form themselves into lines of light which proceed to develop an animated four-fold movement. These vivid lines take on a swaying rhythmic motion as they interlace in light spirals throughout space. From these, more lines are continuously born which tumble into place and create simple forms. Within such shapes I am aware of energy forming into substance which is both irridescent and seemingly gelatinous. Globules of colour emerge from these light forms and contain, I believe, the original pattern and essence of all life.

This magnetic field plays the role of the condenser of all experience which enters the physical body from without; it is capable of sifting through its mesh-like substance all atmospheric radiations of light, sound, colour and movement. This makes the magnetic field surrounding each human organism the receptor and reflector of all 'supernormal' as well as normal perceptions which eventually reach the human organism.

When experience is received within the magnetic field, I see it as then passing through the body in a series of light rays which move rhythmically in and out in a swift and continuous succession. The field is able to participate in the ceaseless changes of the physical body through an inner process, whereby the light rays register, unfailingly, the design of the daily living throughout the physical, mental, and other bodily states of the human organism.

I always examine the condition of the magnetic field which envelops the body of the person with whom I work clairvoyantly. It is by the state of this field that I am able, according to its clarity and particular colours, to judge the degree of physical, mental and emotional vitality and health of the individual. Colour plays a most important part in signifying the state of well being and emotional stress in the field of each person.

I have often been able to trace within the magnetic field, lines and breaks which tell me what specific disease or illness a person has had. My analyses of such 'scars' have been verified on many occasions. To those who know its language of signs and colours, man's magnetic field becomes a kind of map by which the condition of the body, mind and spirit is clearly disclosed. So does this field play a decisive role in the development of man's personality. I hope that Science will soon become aware of the existence of the magnetic field as the diagnostic chart of the state of man's entire being.

As to the character of this energy field, we are told that it is suctional and inward acting, in contrast to the expansive tendencies of ponderable matter. To Steiner, the *ether* element is a form of negative mass, a hollowing-out of space. There is matter which has an outward, repelling, and reflecting effect, and its complement in the etheric hole which absorbs and integrates. Positive matter tends to disperse, while negative ether binds, creating form and structure. In the cyclic flow of energy between matter and ether, only the outward physical flow can be observed with physical perception.

This view of the ether is somewhat different from the scientific *aether* which comes and goes in scientific theories. For some time now, mainly through the influence of quantum theory, it has been out of fashion. But it is still a live issue. Scientists have not forgotten Paul Dirac's imaginative thinking that led to the concept of the antiparticle – the electromagnetic antithesis of the subatomic particle. He put forward the idea that the whole of space might consist of electrons of *negative mass*: and when these are forced to make the quantum jump into positive mass, they leave behind holes with just the right characteristics for the anti-electron. This was in fact discovered about a year later, much to the amazement of the scientific community.

In Indian thought, the all-pervasive akasa, or akasha, is the universal cosmic matter from which all other energy is ultimately derived. It exists in two complementary forms: there is the passive and mechanistic akasa naturally related to the nineteenth century aether for the propagation of electromagnetic waves; and there is the active and vitalising akasa akin to the esoteric ether, and perhaps to Dirac's aether. For the moment, physicists are trying to do without either concept, with light waves replaced by infinite streams of photons, and all field forces, whether cohesive or repellent, being rationalised in terms of discrete interactions between particles.

The etheric concept of esoteric thought is not essentially contradictory to modern energy ideas. The forces of gravitation, magnetism, and nuclear cohesion – about which we understand the least – all have integrative properties. Recent theorising about collapsing stars and black holes also has obvious associations. It can be regarded as just a different way of expressing things, with two distinct categories of inward and outward forces. But the idea of two complementary processes involving action and reaction between two subspaces is a more flexible formulation than what we have at the moment in science. It is a concept applicable from the solar system right down to the atomic level. In the atomic nucleus and the electron bands, in the nucleus and cytoplasm of the cell, in the endoderm and ectoderm of the embryo, in the medulla and cortex of the major organs, there are these inner-outer processes at work. At all levels, physical and etheric, Yin and Yang, together produce field and frequency patterns that generate the phenomenal world.

On a universal level, we can conceive the etheric forces as constituting a whole domain complementary to the observable universe – this only being visible to us because of the reflective properties of matter. To our physical senses, aided by physical instrumentation, the physical universe naturally appears to be continually expanding. But from a more general cosmic viewpoint, this can be regarded as a relative perception dependent on our specific visual systems.

However, monist science and philosophy is exceptionally sensitive about any such dualist formulation, wanting no suggestion of any domain separate from, yet interacting with, the physical. It leads all too obviously to dangerous spiritualistic conceptions. Therefore etheric ideas about negative mass must be left as an interesting Dirac eccentricity.

Regardless of current fashions, the spiritualists continue to write extensively about an earth-bound etheric domain complementary to our physical space-time. Most orthodox scientists dismiss this immediately without ever looking into it, and it has to be left to independent spirits like Alfred Wallace, or Frederic Myers, or William James to investigate objectively. While each came to different conclusions about the evidence, all were agreed that in the exploration of psychical and memory structure, here was something of absolutely fundamental interest and importance. And without any specific research, many have found that, when faced directly with certain visual and aural evidence, it is impossible to dismiss, or simply reduce to subjective psychological statements. The evidence presented, for instance, by Sir Oliver Lodge, or Bishop Pike, to take two celebrated cases, is completely in line with spiritualist philosophy. Both men were distinguished by their rationality, and general unwillingness to interpret unusual phenomena in terms outside conventional Western viewpoints or scientific theory. Both lost a son just as they were coming to manhood, and both have written in depth about their contact with an etheric world closely related to the earth energies. It is worth noting that Bishop Pike, like most theologians, was very sceptical about any form of survival 'now'; and he had in fact much in common with the mental attitudes of an agnostic humanist.

Their evidence suggests a world coexisting with ours, having many similarities with physical experience, although with greater awareness of the power of thought and feeling. Scenically it is much the same; and, although there is nothing corresponding to physical pain, mental suffering and emotional disturbance remain part of the pattern of life. One gets an impression of a world 'written on the back' of this world. Relating it to the modern study of dyslexia, this could be more than a vague symbolic statement. There is certainly the implication of some sort of perceptual inversion.

In general, the esotericists have held the view that spiritualist phenomena, although not in any way fraudulent, were likely to be misunderstood or misinterpreted. And after many years as a medium, Eileen Garrett began to reject conventional spiritualist explanations, and turned towards science and psychology for alternative rationalisations. Buddhists consider that communication with the real spiritual planes of existence is simply impossible: only those who have just died, or had their lives prematurely terminated through accident or suicide, could be contacted in the limbo etheric world. Where there seemed to be contact with those who had died naturally and passed into the devachanic regions, one was not in fact communicating with spirits, but with the lower etheric or astral shells that are progressively shed in the evolution towards the higher planes. At each level, one is supposed to retain just the inner core or essence necessary for each vibrational level. The lower shells have a consciousness, but it could be a very misleading one, being possibly at odds with the higher self.

This explanation appears consistent with at least some of the evidence, although not all. What sometimes come through in trance are certain superficial characteristics of a person as he was about the time of death. There is a basic consciousness, but the deeper aspects of the mind may be completely missing. It could be that the mind of the medium to some extent fills in the shells, and works through them. Eileen Garrett wondered if her controls were of this nature, feeding, so to speak, on her own subconscious. But to the end, her controls maintained the validity of their own individual existence and identity. With all the new evidence from hypnotic regression of past lives, and of disturbed people who dissociate into multiple personalities, it would seem that each subconscious contains a number of entities which, in certain cases, do not integrate naturally with the new developing mind.

Some interpret the evidence in terms of a cosmic or earth memory; others in terms of telepathy between subconscious minds. Eileen Garrett came to realise that much could be explained in terms of *psychometry*, in that inanimate objects seem to be impregnated with magnetic vibrations that produce elementary pictorial information for the clairvoyant mind. But until we have a deeper understanding of psychical structure, it is not possible to draw many positive conclusions.

All this is largely ignored by academic psychologists, although they are prepared to admit the existence of multiple personality. In this state, what may be called the 'primary entity' appears to opt out completely – generally under stress – and a separate entity emerges to take over all conscious functioning. There may in fact be several other entities ready to take over, each one having a distinctive personality and memory content.

Probably the most remarkable case of recent times is that of 'Sybil', who under careful psychoanalysis, exhibited no less than sixteen personalities – two male and the remainder female. Her childhood was a terrible torment, and from adolescence onwards, the primary Sybil found herself losing all conscious knowledge of whole days and weeks, even once of a period extending to over a year. She had no idea what happened during the intervening times; and it was only under psychiatric investigation that she was able to learn of the existence of the other entities – although they were very much aware of Sybil and her problems. Eventually, through hypnotic methods, the various personalities were integrated into some general consensus viewpoint compatible with Sybil.

Whether we interpret this as a case of one personality split into many parts, or of a damaged new personality taken over by stronger subconscious entities, or a mixture of the two, it does suggest most positively the existence of discrete psychical systems having a certain independence from each other, and from the body. Fortunately, the evidence is not in dispute in the Sybil case as it was obtained over several years by orthodox professional methods.

Allied to such phenomena suggestive of discarnate states are the near-death, and other out-of-body or projection experiences that are at last being seriously investigated. For most of this century, it has been impossible to discuss such matters in any scientific context. The evidence was very intermittent, and so could easily be ignored. It also ran completely contrary to materialist dogma. But with more people prepared to make their evidence public, and also with modern hormonal techniques of resuscitation, we are now getting some systematic information from scientific and medical sources.

Interesting work has been done by Robert Crookall in quietly collecting and collating evidence of this nature over many years. The classic work of Sylvan Muldoon about his own projection experiences is now quite widely known. Eileen Garrett has also written informatively on the subject. However, many who have described their out-of-body sensations had little or no prior knowledge of these matters. At a certain point of time, something happened to them that was so real and vivid, and so different in quality from the routine waking consciousness, that it became the most significant event, the most treasured memory of their lives.

Naturally, describing such an abnormal experience through normal language is something of a problem. But whatever the terminology used, the meaning is generally fairly clear, with certain common aspects described over and over again. Of special importance to rational enquiry, particularly for the further understanding of the perceptual processes, are the descriptions of spatially distant events, and the detailed accounts of medical operations on the physical body. These are verifiable matters which will only be ignored by the prejudiced mind.

In the out-of-body state, one becomes conscious of the physical body as a separate entity. This is the common denominator of all such experience – a vivid and sure understanding that there are at least two of you. Many also comment on the aural field surrounding the physical body., and a silver cord linking the two bodies. Most see and hear fairly normally, although the light is subdued and without shadows. The return to the body is likely to cause a sudden shudder, and subsequent feelings of dizziness and nausea.

Psychologically, the return is accompanied by a sense of disappointment, and a general dulling of the senses. In the projected state, the person can feel that much more alive, and the senses so much more acute. As sometimes occurs in hypnosis, objects can be seen at considerable distances, the ticking of a watch can be heard in another room, and the subject can identify people through smell as animals do. It is interesting that a hypnotic subject may even become aware of the sensations of the hypnotist, including taste, and the sense of whether it is pleasurable or not.

In Yoga, we are told that such a release may occur when the kundalini energy of the lowest centre is forced upwards through the other centres to the crown of the head. To do this is considered to be very difficult, requiring many years of practice in developing conscious control of the correct channelling of energies through the intermediate centres of the spinal cord. Uncontrolled release, through spinal injury for instance, may accidentally happen to anyone, sometimes with unfortunate symptoms of psychotic behaviour. But with due preparation and guidance, it is claimed to be an unrivalled form of therapy, releasing dormant energies which give a new creative outlook to the individual, and freeing him from many forms of ill-health. However, the real purpose of Yoga is not such a psychical release, but a joining, or yoking, with the universal Consciousness.

Because of their subjective nature, too much emphasis cannot be placed on these unusual experiences. But in all things, it is the totality of evidence that counts. As much of it relates closely to aspects of hypnosis which, for most people, is established well beyond any scientific scepticism, there is definite reason to study the details of the evidence. We note that much of abnormal psychology involves one of two complementary processes: either external projection in space, or internal regression in time. Such a perceptual dualism in the experience of space and time is an important concept, and one that we will return to several times in the course of the book.

Unfortunately parapsychologists have spent far too long looking over their shoulders towards the respectable monism of science and theology, and consequently missed important opportunities of breaking new ground in the psychology of perceptual states. Early on they decided to try to establish the existence of mental communication between two people on a statistical basis through wearisome card-guessing games. To Eileen Garrett when subjected to these random experiments, a guess was simply a guess; and without emotional or purposeful content, it was a pointless exercise. But to this day, psychically-gifted people are still subject to these repetitive procedures, and still as bored as ever.

If a person is able to describe in detail events going on a hundred miles away, or a hundred years ago, then we are not concerned with statistical probability, but with fundamental problems about how the perceptual systems function. We do not know how they work through the normal visual processes – just what goes on in the back of the brain is a great mystery. But this we find is just one specialised process of seeing in space-time. From all the evidence, it would seem that both space-distant and time-distant events can be captured in some mental way – by a few people naturally, and by many people when induced by some method into a different state of perceptual consciousness.

For hard, consistent evidence in this area, the information coming through the subconscious of Edgar Cayce over a period of forty years is likely to be the most significant for some time to come. Nearly every day, after being cured for a throat condition by hypnosis, Cayce would go into a self-hypnotic state, and answer detailed questions – medical, historical, personal, scientific, psychological – from individual people who in general wanted some sort of diagnosis and understanding of their difficulties. These life-readings were given to many thousands of people; and the great virtue of this work is that the information was fully recorded, and followed up or checked out as far as humanly possible. Remote perception in space seemed no problem for the Cayce subconscious, nor regression to anyone else's past. Day after day, apparently moving freely in space and time, Cayce expounded on complex subjects, and provided detailed medical diagnoses and remedies.

Yet the conscious Cayce was a simple Christian person, thoughtful but not well-read or well-educated. Much of the information he found quite bewildering, and it was a long time before he began to trust it. The refreshing thing about it all was that he had no particular axe to grind, no new movement to found; there was no quest for power, or a need to impress, and no financial exploitation. The medical material was not geared to just one approach, but involved a whole spectrum of therapies and techniques. In Cayce, all the fascinating aspects of abnormal perceptual phenomena come together in a unique and penetrating way. Here is a substantial and organised body of knowledge, making much eminent sense, and seriously challenging the orthodox assumptions of today.

His contributions to human knowledge take us right away from the sterile and simplistic arguments that have gone on about the Theory of Evolution over the last hundred years. To understand the Cayce material, one has to perceive the psyche, neither as an instant creation nor as the chance emanation of genetic forces, but as the product of a long continuous process of distillation and purification through many forms of experience, very gradually becoming more individualised and self-aware, and able to control increasingly complex forms. In each life, a new personality is developed; and through the course of time, the memories associated with this life recede into the subconscious background.

Through these far-memories, Cayce seems to have come to the same basic conclusions about world history as can be found in theosophical literature. Man has already reached advanced stages at least once before; and what we now term 'esoteric' are the subconscious remnants of this period. The fragments of understanding that have survived through Grecian, Egyptian, Indian, and Chinese cultures are naturally difficult for the modern academic mind to grasp working through the restricted thought-forms and assumptions currently fashionable. They are also obscured by the more recent uncivilised past of most entities – which incidentally encourages psychologists in the belief that the subconscious contains only primitive material that is holding back human progress.

But most of Cayce's regression material goes much further back than is now being attempted by modern hypnotherapy, and points to new interpretations of our development. On his evidence, we are now in the process, not of discovery, but of rediscovery. And it remains to be seen once again whether we will be mature enough to use our knowledge, both technical and psychical, constructively.

This whole area of hypnosis, self-hypnosis, and regression, constitutes a reliable and verifiable form of experimentation into the human psyche. In fact, compared with much complex and costly scientific experiment today, it would appear to be a particularly direct avenue to new knowledge. By comparison, the atomic physicist, for instance, has now to rely on the laws of probability, or a fair amount of luck, that a specific event may occur within perhaps several thousand experiments; while in biochemical research, the body needs only the tiniest emotional trigger to produce enormous and unrepeatable changes in electrochemical and hormonal activity. Research into the hypnotic state, whether of a perceptual nature, or exploring the subconscious memory, or in the mental control over the autonomics of the body, provides evidence that is consistent and replicable.

This paranormal information of hypnosis has been available to the

Western world for almost two hundred years since Mesmer and his contemporaries established the various phenomenal aspects. And as few would now dispute the phenomena, we would be wise to concentrate on this 'third state' of man, rather than the contentious material associated with unusual individual powers. It is still quite fashionable for medical theorists to laugh at Mesmer's theories regarding some impenetrable fluid with magnetic properties, but Mesmer was clearly ahead of his time. He and later nineteenth century investigators tried to understand the phenomena in terms of field forces, in contrast to modern psychologists who have resorted to vague subjective terms. It would now appear that we will move back towards earlier electromagnetic theorising on this subject, and interest in the changing field and frequency patterns. With the new forms of cerebral and whole-body imaging, such as those involving positrons and magnetic resonance, we should now be in a position to obtain important comparisons of waking, sleep, and trance states.

In recent years, we have acquired important new evidence of subconscious activity through the phenomenon of *mutual hypnosis*, in which one hypnotised person draws another into the trance state. In this process, the two subjects go into their own mental world, and together explore their new plane of consciousness. They communicate telepathically, and sometimes experience an idyllic soul relationship separate from their physical bodies. The scientific importance of this mutual hypnotic procedure is that, when the account of the experience from one subject correlates with that of the other, then we have a definite objective experience to evaluate. With just one hypnotised person, descriptive material which cannot be independently verified can be passed off as the product of the imagination. But with these mutual experiences, and no physical passing of information, we obtain evidence for direct mental communication.

Public interest in hypnosis tends to centre on regression procedures, and the exploration of long-term memory. Some most interesting information has been published by Dr Helen Wambach who has regressed hundreds of people. She has been particularly interested in the birth experience, and all that led up to the decision to be born. Most seemed to feel a great reluctance to enter into physical existence again, although a few had well thought-out plans. Most complained of bright lights, cold, and an uncaring atmosphere in which they first found themselves. In general, there was a clear consciousness of joining the foetus just before birth. Clearly such information is very pertinent to modern debates about childbirth and abortion.

The work of Arnall Bloxham, the Welsh hypnotherapist, is equally absorbing, and centres on historical information. Because some of the regressions were done so openly with TV cameras, there has been a massive effort to discredit him, or to find alternative rationalisations. But to historical scholars, his evidence has held up extremely well, and led on to some new studies. The subconscious memory not only corroborates known facts, but can also set the record straight in doubtful areas. Academic resistance to such studies is gradually fading, and the University of California in particular has been very active in this area.

At the other end of the hypnotic spectrum, there are phenomena which seem to involve communication with a cerebral automaton having a neutral, indifferent, even callous attitude to the finer feelings of the soul. It will obey orders without question, even to the extent of throwing acid at an experimenter – leaving the confused conscious mind to try to rationalise the action afterwards. In post-hypnotic suggestion, it will override the conscious controls with absurd activity, regardless of the embarrassing consequences. If so instructed, it will make ammonia influence the senses like perfume, and perfume like ammonia. And when told to change its normal 3-dimensional visual picture to a 2-dimensional one, the subject will curl up into a foetal position, and experience the environment caving in. This automaton was the subject of much earlier research, but the accent today is shifting towards more conscious oversight of the trance state.

Surveying the evidence of his time, and arguing every viewpoint, William James could only suggest rather vague pluralist concepts. Wallace, on the other hand, was thoroughly convinced of a spiritualist interpretation (this being quite compatible with a generalised view of evolution). Freud, although restricted by an intense antagonism to all occult ideas, resurrected the concept of the unconscious mind. Edgar Cayce came reluctantly to accept a reincarnational viewpoint. Frederic Myers conceived of a broad psychical spectrum involving differing balances between the subliminal and supraliminal mind, and extending in some cases to spirit entities beyond the self. He perhaps above all others made the bravest attempt, from a Western viewpoint, to classify all the known phenomena of abnormal psychology, from automatism, schizophrenia, multiple personality, and possession, to clairvoyant and regression states. Today, these matters are returning for renewed consideration; and with our more detailed physical knowledge, and greater awareness of Eastern thought-forms, we should get things in better perspective, and improve on earlier theories and interpretations.

3. Eastern and Western Physiology

Concepts about the higher systems discussed in the last chapter are not immediately translatable into modern scientific terms. Naturally, if there are systems distinct from material and cellular forms, everyone wants to know how we can go about studying them, and what relationship they have to Western categories of nerve, hormone, blood, lymph, muscle, and bone. Fortunately, in the specifically Eastern physiologies associated with Yoga and acupuncture, there are more detailed thought-forms that appear to have a direct bearing on many modern Western studies, including endocrine structure and behavioural effects of hormones, conscious and autonomic activity, psychosomatic therapies, and general psychical research. Yoga philosophy is in fact a bridge between the objective physical studies of the body, and the vaguer esoteric concepts about the higher systems, and makes a great deal of sense of both. Today, we have adepts doing research at high levels in hormone chemistry, and we have Western doctors endeavouring to use Yoga methods in conjunction with endocrine treatment.

One of the most distinguished Western writers in this field was Sir John Woodroffe who wrote extensively on Yoga philosophy and practice. Sir John combined a conventional legal career in colonial India with an intense devotion to its ancient culture and Sanskrit literature; and he has been described as an Eastern soul in a Western body. He understood theosophical ideas and aims, but, like Jung, doubted the wisdom of certain forms of expression, considering that Western attempts to translate Sanskrit terms were liable to lead to a misinterpretation of Indian philosophy. In terms of relevance to the purely physical evidence from the Western sciences, he has probably been proved correct in this.

Yoga philosophy begins from the concept of a pure, changeless, and static Consciousness that precedes all manifestation; and from this all-pervading source, a dynamic consciousness evolves through an innate desire for the creation of particular forms. This dynamic aspect expresses itself from the mental level right down to physical matter, everything being a variant of akasic energy. Thus, we are told, Consciousness becomes Power; and from Power comes mind and matter. And the ultimate possible attainment of the Yogi is the return to the primordial Consciousness that is beyond, or behind, all finite activities of mind, and all specific forms and phenomena associated with emotional and physical sensation.

Clearly, this final state has little or no relevance to scientific studies. In science, and in life generally, it is the diversity of things that concern us, and the relation of one thing to another. The ultimate 'unitary' state, which is essentially a religious and personal experience, is beyond all categories, and beyond all rational analysis. So perhaps it is just worth saying at this point that it is a little difficult to understand those scientific writers who are looking towards such mindless mystical states for insight into scientific problems. Undoubtedly, the possibility of living beyond experience and sensation is an interesting one, but it has no relevance to the problems of physical life. It is worth noting that Paul Brunton, after long years of Eastern meditation and with several books written on the subject, eventually renounced this way simply because it had no answers for normal experience. In fact, he maintained that one could never hold these transcendental states for long – forces were always at work pushing you back to normal levels of consciousness.

However, the dynamic action of Consciousness takes us into the real world of objective-subjective duality, and human individuality. Within this 'separated' self, there are, according to Yoga philosophy, three bodies: the gross material body pervaded and sustained by various life-forces; the subtle body containing the mind and the senses; and the causal body which is the expression of individual consciousness, and the link with the universal Consciousness. The causal body creates and supports the subtle body, and this in turn controls the physical body. The subtle body contains seven main control centres from the base of the spine to the crown of the head – although the highest centre is sometimes regarded as the causal body itself. All the centres have interesting connections with the endocrine glands and hormone activity, and consequently with the nervous system (figures 3.1, 3.2).

In Western terms, the nervous system and the endocrine system are the two principal control mechanisms of the physical body, and they interact through chemical action at the nerve junctions. The nervous system gives more or less immediate responses to internal and external stimuli, in contrast to endocrine processes which provide longer-term controls over physical, emotional, and mental development. This is not to say that hormones are directly responsible for body growth or intellectual activity, but they do undoubtedly have retarding or accelerating effects on many human systems, and

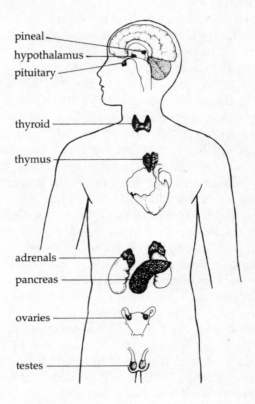

pineal
hypothalamus
pituitary

thyroid

thymus

adrenals
pancreas

ovaries

testes

Fig. 3.1   Hormone centres

removal of glands can cause serious complications or death. Today, many hormones can be artificially synthesised, or isolated out, and so we can determine physical and psychical effects of specific hormone processes. Just how they exert their control, and how they find their way through the blood stream to the target areas, is far from being understood. Like the mysteries of cell co-ordination and communication, they appear to be under the control of invisible directing forces. The main requisite for the efficient functioning of an endocrine gland is a liberal supply of blood.

Together, nerves and hormones form the autonomic neuroendocrine processes which take care of the internal organs by means of suitable activating or inhibiting effects. The central control area of these processes is situated in the *hypothalamus* at the top of the brainstem in a region that will sometimes be referred to as the *thalamic core*

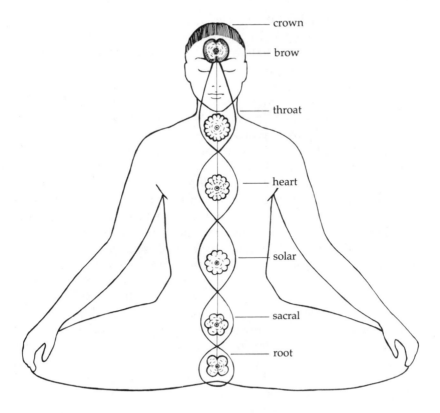

Fig. 3.2   Yoga chakral centres

of the brain. This, as far as brain studies can ascertain, is the highest integrative centre for all cerebral activity, and links the cortical hemispheres with all parts of the body.

Just below the hypothalamus, and closely linked to it, is the *pituitary* gland which is generally considered to be the controlling gland for all hormone activity. On the posterior side of the thalamic core is the *pineal* gland in a region more related to conscious control of the body. For most people, the autonomics of nerves and hormones continue with little conscious direction from the central nervous system; and one of the aims of Yoga is to develop direct mental control over these unconscious processes.

In Sir John Woodroffe's day, little was known about the hormone system, and the only correlations attempted concern the nervous system – particularly the spinal cord and the autonomic chains of neurons on either side of it. He tells us that the five lower centres are located within the spinal cord, and correspond with the five principal sections of conventional anatomy – coccyx, sacral, lumbar, thoracic, and cervical. Conscious activity is mediated through the central spinal channel from the thalamic or *crown* centre; and autonomic activity is regulated from the hypothalamus, or *brow* centre through energy pathways on either side of the spine. However, there is the complication that Yoga pathways involve two complementary coils of energy rather than the direct nerve chains of orthodox anatomy.

From the psychic centres, we are told, thousands of energy pathways (*nadis*) emanate connecting to all parts of the body, and to other centres. The overall effect is a set of whirling disc patterns (*chakras*) of lotus form, each with a specific number of petals. There are distinctive colours, ranging from crimson in the root to white at the brow, suggesting perhaps a cumulative colour effect proceeding up the spine. Specific sounds are also associated with each centre; and continuous intoning of certain notes, or *mantras*, stimulates selected centres. Of the thousands of nadis throughout the body, there are fourteen channels of energy considered to be of special importance.

Although the chakras are invisible to normal sight, there are people who say they observe them in waking consciousness without any form of self-hypnosis. There are also suggestions of chakral effects from brain surgery, for when the occipital or visual cortex is touched with a low-frequency electronic probe, whirling disc patterns are often observed. Just pressing the eyelids gently may also produce such effects.

But the most objective evidence for these patterns comes from EEG research. When the brain is subjected to a rapidly flickering light, all sorts of perceptual disturbances are produced. In particular, when the flicker frequency approximates to the major alpha rhythm of about 10 cycles per second, Catherine wheel effects are often observed. In his book, *The Living Brain*, W. Grey Walter relates such phenomena to a visual scanning system, and speculates that the whirling spirals indicate the path taken by the scanning point in the pattern it makes every tenth of a second.

To the biochemist, the form of the vitalising kundalini energy should be of immense interest. According to ancient Tantric literature, the kundalini is in the form of a double coil or helix, with complementary chains of Yin and Yang energies. In the lowest centre, it is said to be coiled three and a half times, and this is reflected in the major energy channels coiling round the spine. This helical force pattern, we are told, is fundamental to all energy levels in the body, whether psychical or physical. Thus it is of great interest that Western science has discovered that the basic genetic material called DNA is structured in this geometrical way.

The lowest, or root chakra is the essential source of kundalini energy and vitalising activity in the body. In the special practices of Kundalini Yoga, the primal energy is guided by mental control upwards toward the crown centre with the object of attaining a blissful unitary state with the universal Consciousness. In more normal terms, this centre relates to sexuality and the male testes, and kundalini practices may be interpreted as a redirection of sexual energy.

Above this is the second or sacral chakra, also a focus of physical vitality and sexuality, and relating to the hormonal activity of the female ovaries. Just whether male and female have both root and sacral centres in their psyche is not made clear in Yoga. However, modern psychological evidence, particularly about homosexuality, and medical evidence from sex-change operations, definitely indicate that we are all both male and female; and making the change from one to the other is largely a matter of psychical emphasis – this being reinforced from the physical side by hormones and surgery. There are suggestions, and understandable ones, that it is unwise to meditate on this centre.

In the stomach area and lumbar section of the spine is the third or solar chakra. This is the instinctive centre, involving a primitive astral consciousness as experienced in dreams. In this region, there are the insulin-producing glands of the pancreas that control sugar levels, sympathetic nerves controlling the lower organs, and the hormonal centres of adrenal medulla and cortex just above the kidneys. Physiologists also recognise this as the instinctive centre, clearly related to fear and aggression. Fear is sensed in the stomach, adrenalin is released from the medulla, the sympathetic nerves are stimulated, blood vessels constrict, and the heart-beat is accelerated. In such times of stress, the adrenal cortex releases cortisone steroids which, along with the parasympathetic division of the nervous system, help to balance the autonomic activity. In normal functioning, the cortex plays a significant part in metabolism, and releases gonadal hormones for the lower sexual centres.

Moving up to the thoracic region, we come to the heart chakra, the centre of human emotion – a view that we have curiously retained in the West in spite of transplant surgery. With the intake of oxygen into the blood stream, and the expulsion of carbon dioxide, it may be seen as the purifying centre of the body. The thymus, just above the heart, also has this purifying role through the hormonal stimulation of the production of lymphocytes which, as part of the white cells of the blood, attack invading organisms. Slowly, medicine is coming to recognise disorders in the heart region in psychosomatic and immunological terms, rather than as the product of bacteria and viruses. Cardiac conditions, and autoimmune diseases where lymphocytes fail to respect the body's own constituents, may have purely physical or environmental origins; but it is now fairly clearly understood that emotional problems and difficult memory material connected with childhood can later in life physically manifest themselves in this region. Treating the heart just as a simple pump is a most dangerous simplicity.

In the neck is the fifth, or throat chakra, sometimes referred to as the lower mind. From a psychical viewpoint, this is related to the development of speech and expression, and quality of voice. From the neurological aspect, the cervical region controls the upper half of the body, and movement of arms and hands and fingers. In hormonal terms, there are the thyroid and parathyroid glands that are known to have a considerable effect on both physical growth and mental development. The neck holds the balance between the cerebral mental forces, and the emotional energies of heart and stomach centres; and in speech, one recognises whether this inclines towards the rational or the emotional. From another viewpoint, it is an abrupt constriction between head and trunk, and thus a potential source of trouble, either physically or psychically. But at the same time, it is a natural centre for treatment in balancing therapies, and also a mediator of energies to the hands in direct healing.

The sixth centre is a white two-petalled lotus just above the two eyes, and perhaps best thought of as a double chakra on which the complementary energy channels coiling round the spine converge. This brow chakra relates to the hypothalamus-pituitary autonomic control centre which keeps the internal processes in balance, and stabilises many parameters to remarkable accuracy, including temperature. From a developmental and functional viewpoint, the pituitary has two quite distinct sections. The posterior section is really part of the hypothalamus, and secretes two hormones, one controlling water balance and the other related to childbirth. The anterior pituitary produces many hormones regulating all the lower centres, and influencing growth, metabolism, and general body chemistry. Psychically, the brow centre is often related to the mental activity of the frontal cortex; but physiological evidence would have to relate it to subconscious or unconscious functions.

Descartes placed the rational consciousness further back in the brain around the pineal gland, and this is more in line with modern ideas. For a long time, the pineal was considered to be the atrophied 'third eye' that is found in some primitive creatures, but which seems to have outlived its usefulness in the course of evolution. It is a most difficult organ to study, lying in the thalamic core of the brain between the two hemispheres. But progress is being made, and it is certainly a far more active organ than has generally been assumed in the past. Through the sympathetic nervous system, it is affected by the environmental lighting which controls the synthesis of melatonin, an important hormone that seems to have effects on the pituitary, the thyroid, the adrenals, and the gonads – although the mechanisms and purposes are far from being understood. It also has the effect of lightening skin pigmentation, in contrast to a pituitary hormone which darkens the skin. Other interesting evidence suggests that the pineal regulates the time of puberty to some extent, so perhaps acting as a long-term clock within the physical system. The hormone production only takes place at night when the external lighting is at a minimum.

Taking all the evidence into account, both ancient and modern, it is impossible to make any physiological correlation for the highest conscious centre, the crown chakra, except in terms of the pineal and posterior thalamic region. Quite apart from the hormonal aspects, this is the central integrative area of the brain, linking the major sensory and motor sections of the cortex to the brainstem and central nervous system. The cerebrospinal channel converges on this region; and according to Yoga description, it is the focus of a thousand-petalled colourless chakra in which all aspects of the other centres are duplicated many times over. While the forward brow sections are related to the two eyes whose optic tracts meet in the hypothalamic region, the crown vortex is thought of as the inner eye which, in conjunction with the visual cortex at the back of the brain, integrates the optic signals and internally recreates the external picture. In some Yoga texts, one finds the interesting thought that the mind simply takes the form of whatever it is looking at.

Many of these ideas will be further developed later in the book. For the moment though, let us just briefly summarise this psychophysiological outline. In the lowest spinal segments, the root and sacral chakras reflect male and female centres of vitality and sexuality. In the middle segments of the spine, the instinctive and emotional chakras interact with the pancreas, adrenals, and thymus. In the cervical region where head and trunk forces merge, the thyroid and parathyroids reflect the activity of the throat chakra generating speech and gesture. And all the centres are regulated from the brow and crown chakras: subconsciously through the autonomic hypothalamic centre to the front of the brain; and consciously through the more posterior region of the thalamus, including the

pineal (or epithalamus). These cerebral centres together, forming
what is called the diencephalon, co-ordinate not only all internal and
peripheral activity, but also the special external senses including
vision.

C. W. Leadbeater has given us fairly detailed personal descriptions
of the centres which in most respects agree with Sir John Woodroffe.
However, his pictures are more dynamic than the Sanskrit texts, and
in some ways more specific. He indicates, for instance, that when the
brow centre is closely scrutinised, each half is seen to have 48 divisions – equivalent to the sum of the five lower centres. In the crown
centre, he has counted precisely 960 divisions in the outer vortex, and
a further twelve in the inner portion. These cerebral centres, shown
as having a common origin in the pineal area, he does not find either
white or colourless, but a wonderful display of spectral colours, particularly violet, yellow, purple, and blue. Does one then make the
tempting assumption that although the Eastern adept may have
attained a perfect physical-psychical balance, his high-minded
detachment produces a very neutral personality without the colour
and warmth that appeals to us in the West?

Leadbeater places the second chakra in the spleen-pancreas region,
rather than the ovaries. However, this may refer to a specifically
female arrangement. He also says that, although the lower centres
appear on the front of the body, they are all linked by a 'stalk' to the
spine. Today, there is a more sophisticated version of this concept,
involving a double cone of energy penetrating the body. The central
vertex lies within the spine, and the two cones at the front and back of
the body have opposite magnetic polarisations.

The psychical-physiological correlations that have been made
should be generally intelligible to both Eastern and Western modes of
thought. Through the chakras and energy channels, the Yoga adept
gains conscious control over many of the body functions that normally are assumed to work only at the unconscious autonomic level.
He can for instance anaesthetise, or magnetise, selected areas of the
body just through mental control – as can be done under hypnosis.
This mental control involves the correct imaging of energy centres
and processes, and coordination with breathing. One breathes in, and
then suitably channels the energies to various parts of the body. The
possibility of this is now coming to be recognised by Western researchers; and there is strong evidence for the viewpoint that the way the
mind communicates with the autonomic nervous system is through
such imaging processes. Therefore, in order to correct imbalances, or
remove physical obstructions, a person must first be given some pictorial form of physiological processes, whether conceived in Western

or Eastern terms.

Working from the physical side, medical scientists have found they can significantly influence physical functions, growth, and general behaviour through changes to the endocrine system, either through removal of specific glands, or through injections of hormone material. Control of ovulation, heart-rate, metabolism, and various other aspects of physical development is fairly well understood in terms of hormone chemistry; and their effects on mental and emotional development are becoming clearer. However, we are coming to re-cognise that there are significant dangers in purely chemical methods. Dependence on hormones, including steroids, inevitably upsets aspects of energy balance and activity in the body, to the extent that it may never recover its equilibrium. Ultimately, improvement must come under the control of higher systems if there is to be any perma-nent change for the better. Yoga aims to make use of the constructive power of thought to bring the various physical systems into balance. However, this requires powers of concentration that comparatively few possess.

With acupuncture, we have a more practical approach to the prob-lems of ill health and disease, yet one which seems to follow the Yoga philosophy. Yoga and acupuncture are not clearly linked in many people's minds, even by some of those practising acupuncture, but the links are all there. As has been stated, the chakral centres are related to the body through the nadis, or life-force channels, and it is these meridians of energy linking the subtle body to the physical body with which acupuncture is concerned. In Yoga theory, there are said to be thousands of these energy channels – Sir John Woodroffe gives the figure of 72,000. But of these, there are twelve pairs of channels on either side of the body, plus two down the centre at front and back that are of primary importance. Numerically, this is the same as in acupuncture, although it is difficult to say from the litera-ture available on this subject if the Yoga and acupuncture channels correspond in general terms.

Taking now a brief look at the basic acupuncture view of physiol-ogy, we note first that the energy in each meridian is supposed to control a particular organ or function – and just how this may be rationalised in Western terms will be discussed later. This life-energy – Prana in Yoga, Qi in acupuncture – is considered to have two major polarities: Yin, the female or earthly, and Yang, the male or cosmic. For good health and correct functioning of the internal organs, the two polarities must be correctly balanced, both in general terms, and through the various relationships existing between the individual meridians. There is a daily cycle (figure 3.3) of Qi flowing sequen-

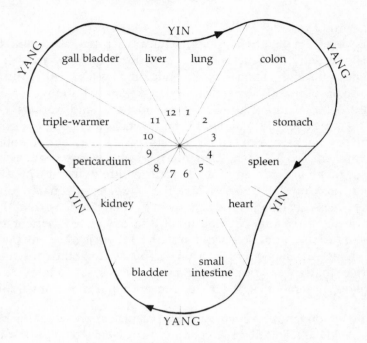

Fig. 3.3   Daily cycle

tially through the asymmetrical meridians, with each meridian being most suitable for balancing operations during an approximate two-hour period each day. As with the side-effects of modern medicine, these balancing operations are not a clear-cut thing, for alterations to one meridian affect others, particularly the 'pre' and 'post' meridians of the daily cycle.

At first glance (figure 3.4), one may perhaps tend to think of the meridian organisation as some primitive irrational view of physiology and anatomy, just as one might have done with the chakras before the discovery of the hormone centres. But there is nothing obviously unreasonable about the overall organisation; and in the cerebral area, the contours relate to aspects of internal brain structure. With the twelve asymmetrical meridians, there is a sensible symmetry about the arms and legs, with three Yin and three Yang meridians linking up through the daily cycle in both feet and hands. The Yin energies are generally to the front of the body, and Yang to the back. If the arms are raised upwards, Yang energies flow downwards, and Yin upwards. Yin meridians begin or end in the thoracic or chest regions, while Yang begin or end in the head. Thus, through both position and function, the Yin energies are suggestive of the sympathetic branch of the nervous system, with its instinctive qualities of arousal; and the Yang of the calming and controlling energies of the parasympathetic system associated with higher cerebral activity.

On the meridians are several hundred acupoints, which can be thought of as minor chakras, or nodal positions of vibrational energy, or points where the meridian ducts surface on the skin. Some biochemical work has purported to show that there are many similar channels, but purely internal, associated with the structuring of particular organs, and that the main meridians are just those nadis that do in fact come to the surface. However, certain theorists and acupuncturists place little or no value on the meridian concept, concerning themselves entirely with the acupoints and their specific effects. This is worth bearing in mind because the concept of a vertical meridian may be just one particular way of associating the points. From the organisation of the peripheral nervous system, a horizontal association looks far more natural to the neurologist.

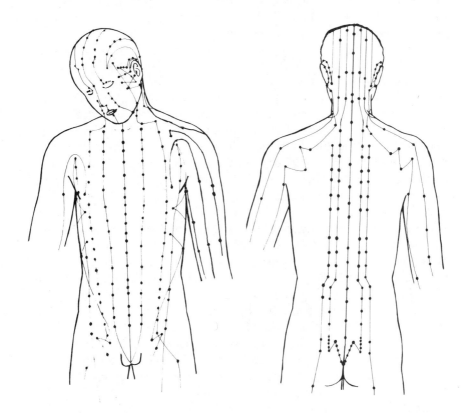

Fig. 3.4   Acupoints and meridians

We now have some scientific methods for finding acupoints, thus enabling us to conduct some straightforward research. There are sophisticated methods involving the use of radioactive phosphorus, and forms of electrical photography that sometimes show special effects at the points. But by far the simplest method is through electrical resistance – the channels between the points being of comparatively low resistance compared with two general points on the skin surface. For low-frequency currents, the change in an average person is something of the order of a million ohms down to a few thousand ohms. Thus a variety of electronic instruments, accommodating individual differences, are now available for discovering these focal positions of energy, and are in daily use in acupuncture clinics. The one positive thing that has been established about the acupoints is that they form a common pattern in normally-developed humans; and the pattern changes according to species.

As now practised, acupuncture of course comes from the Chinese. On its own, without the help of Yoga or neuroendocrine ideas, it is difficult to follow, and could well be a little muddled. But one must take into account that it is based on at least three thousand years of investigation and treatment, not only on humans, but on animals as well. Those who argue today that it is all psychosomatic have obviously not taken this latter fact into consideration. Essentially it is preventive medicine, regarding physical symptoms as an advanced effect of something that has probably been out of balance for a considerable time. The aim of the traditional Chinese doctor is to keep people in good health, with ill health representing failure. Meridian flows must be kept in balance, and the acupoints need to be checked at regular intervals. Unfortunately in Western medicine, we have no such checks, and our doctors have little insight into what troubles might lie ahead.

Traditional theory and practice have become exceedingly complex over the centuries, and the accent now in the West is on simplification of theory, and experimentation with new forms of energy input. Some clinics, for instance, use just three acupoints for each meridian: a test point, a sedation point, and a stimulation point. Among medical researchers, there is a natural preference for the new developing electro-acupuncture where input is effected through electronic pulses – either direct to the skin, or to inserted needles. Others are using sonic impulses, and a few are trying to evaluate electromagnetic field input from simple coils. However, these more technological methods have their own problems because so little is known as yet about suitable voltages, or frequency, or energy intensity. If these are unsuitably set, harm may be done.

The associated Japanese art of Shiatsu avoids both needles and pulses, simply using finger pressure. This gives us a link with osteopathy, and the spinal techniques used in chiropractic. It also has associations with natural or spiritual healing in that various body centres are stimulated through the hands and fingers of another person. In fact, most of natural therapeutics can be rationalised in a general way in terms of energy-centres activating neuro-endocrine mechanisms. And between the sexes, this type of healing and balancing is a continuous process.

An interesting development in recent years has been that of auricular acupuncture which uses just the ear for diagnosis and treatment. The form of the ear is regarded as the human embryo, with head downwards, and corresponding parts of the ear are related to the complete form of the body. Using a sonic oscillator to detect significant changes in electrical resistance, there would seem to be considerable potential in the diagnostic aspect at least. This is certainly amenable to clear-cut testing; and recent American studies have shown this aspect in a favourable light.

Through such studies, a certain credibility barrier is being broken down, and orthodox Western doctors are beginning to take an active interest. By and large, a theory based on life-forces and meridian flows has little appeal. Felix Mann, for instance, who has probably done as much as anyone for the acupuncture cause, slowly came to reject the meridian concept as a form of energy flow, although finding the idea useful in categorising points, and in envisaging pain pathways. To him, the acupoints have a definite relationship with the nervous system, and particularly with the *dermatomes* which represent the distribution areas to the surface of the body of the 31 spinal nerves (figure 3.5). They also relate to *myotome* and *sclerotome* regions linking muscle and bone areas with spinal nerves. These nerves have direct connections with the autonomic chains. Therefore, for a simple explanation of acupuncture techniques, we can envisage that the inserted needle activates a particular nerve back to its spinal or vertebral position, and thence stimulates associated autonomic nerves that control internal processes and organs. In so doing, hormones relating to emotional tone, and other neurotransmitters to the perception of pain, are released from the nerve endings. This is a straightforward rationalisation of acupuncture quite devoid of any mysticism, and consistent with known facts.

However, this is all rather general. More specific and reasonably intelligible in Western terms are the *points of association* on the bladder meridian on either side of the spine which relate spinal position to internal organ and meridian. These are the twelve major control

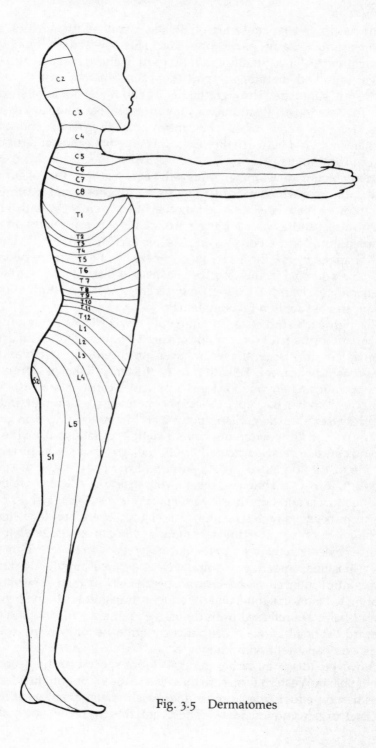

Fig. 3.5   Dermatomes

points for the internal processes of the body, and simply by pressing them, we are told, suitable balancing effects result. Therefore, this gives us a very simplified although quite comprehensive form of acupuncture that could be understood and practised by anyone.

The association-point concept of acupuncture is broadly in line with the neurological diagram shown in figure 3.6, but it suggests there exists a simple one-one correspondence between spinal position and internal organ – neurology indicating, for some organs, several connections to the spine, and passing through complex nerve centres like the solar plexus. Between Eastern and Western understandings, small and large intestine positions seem to be reversed, and here one suspects a simple mistake in acupuncture tradition. The acupuncture correspondence is as follows.

spinal nerve position	meridian/organ
T3	lung
T5	pericardium
T6	heart
T9	liver
T10	gall-bladder
T11	pancreas/spleen
T12	stomach
L1	triple-warmer (see chapter 7)
L2	kidney
L4	large intestine (colon)
S2	small intestine
S3	bladder

The subject of referred pain in medical literature has much in common with these ideas. This relates certain skin areas where pain is likely to be felt as a result of malfunctioning of an internal organ. The usual rationale for this is basically the same as just given for acupuncture – if the autonomic nerves and peripheral nerves of the skin converge on the same spinal segment, then the internal disturbance is likely to be 'referred' to the skin by the peripheral system. But until very recently, the reverse line of reasoning had never really been seriously considered – the surgeon treating the internal organ directly rather than working through related areas of skin and innervation of peripheral nerves. Acupuncture theory and practice thus might fill this gap in our medical knowledge in a most comprehensive way.

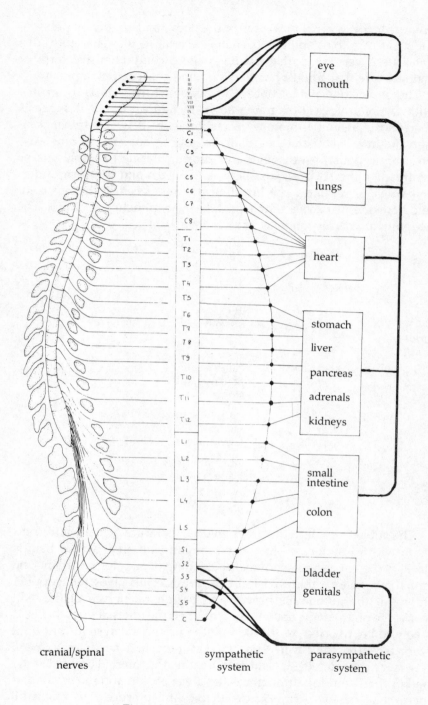

cranial/spinal   sympathetic   parasympathetic
nerves   system   system

Fig. 3.6   Human nervous system

Our Western approach has so many shortcomings because we have few ideas about the structural forces of the body. The surgeon diagnoses a disturbance here, a growth there, and generally attempts to treat the body locally without too much consideration about possible causes from other parts. He removes important glands in one area, and refuses to relate it to massive effects in another area. He attempts to eradicate pain by cutting spinal nerves, but may leave the patient in worse condition. In acupuncture, there is at least an overall theory about mind and body and life-forces, and a natural appreciation that physical pain at one point may relate to energy activity somewhere else.

Comparison of acupuncture and conventional medical practice can be quite striking. For instance, where there is a shortening of one leg, orthodox treatment will generally resort to crude traction methods. With acupuncture, this condition is sometimes cured within minutes on the principle of releasing muscle tension in the shorter leg. Western medicine has no answer for drug addiction – in fact, is the source of much of it. Yet a little acupuncture to the ear can soon bring relief, and lead to a complete cure. Intense neuralgic pains can be brought under immediate control through pressure on an appropriate acupoint, and major surgery can be performed using similar analgesic methods. Mental illness is also treated by acupuncture, working on the assumption of some energy malfunction preventing mind and body working together.

But above all else, the acupuncturist aims to prevent illness rather than cure or remove physical symptoms. Unlike the Western doctor who has few diagnostic facilities to warn of approaching dangers, the acupuncturist expects to be able to anticipate the physical stage of disease by studying the balance of complementary life-energies and processes. Ultimately he is judged not by his ability to cure and contain, but by his ability to maintain good health.

To be able to do this with some consistency involves long years of study and experience, and the development of special sensitivities, including for instance the reading of twelve separate pulses – six on each wrist – and many different characteristics for each pulse. However, there is no reason why anyone should not be able to appreciate the general functional nature of the Yin-Yang forces within the body. This alone should help to keep the autonomic systems healthily balanced.

The sperm is the Yang, and its correlate in the fully developed organism is the brain and spinal cord. Thus the back of the body to the top of the head are the extremes of Yang in the human organism – leaving the front and lower parts basically Yin. This concept, together with the complementary idea of Yang predominating in the cortical and outer regions, and Yin in the nuclear and inner regions, gives us the general geography of Yin and Yang. In disease and sickness, Yang symptoms involve feverishness and heat in the upper and outer regions, while Yin conditions are characterised by cold and listlessness.

This would suggest some very simple precautions to ensure that the Yang areas are gently cooled and the Yin areas gently warmed. In modern living conditions, sudden temperature changes can so easily bring about unbalanced conditions – which, with our Western conditioning, we like to attribute exclusively to bugs and viruses. While any imbalance may encourage the growth of harmful organisms, it would seem preferable to encourage an intelligent awareness of the polarising energies in the body, rather than attack the chemical symptoms with medical drugs.

Now that acupuncture can be clearly related to electrical and chemical effects that are easily replicated, attitudes among medical researchers are radically changing. And among therapists, there are the beginnings of a quiet revolution. The following amusing and pertinent letter to *The Lancet*, the most orthodox of medical publications, reflects the way this is taking place.

The Lancet, June 13, 1981

BACK PAIN AND ACUPUNCTURE

SIR,—I was interested in your May 2 editorial on back pain. As a physician who is a regular sufferer from the 'idiopathic type' I fully sympathise with my similarly afflicted patients and share with them the painful realisation that all conventional treatments are pretty useless. Your editorial did not mention one line of therapy that has been available for thousands of years, well before analgesics, local anaesthetics, and so on, yet continues to be shunned by doctors and medical journals alike – namely, acupuncture. My own personal experience this week has totally changed my view on this unorthodox therapy.

Five days into the throes of acute back pain with increasing muscle spasm and pain and the increasing assumption of a Groucho Marx posture led me, without much optimism, to turn to acupuncture as a last resort. Contrary to my assumption, this was a very painful procedure. I was assured by my therapist that relief would be virtually immediate. To my chagrin I could not leave the couch. The pain was worse, the spasm almost tetanic. Angry doctor intimating dismay to increasingly blushing therapist. Doctor now walking out of surgery like Groucho Marx with kyphosis. Crawls into car, 30 minute drive home. Doctor convinced that he had been 'had' – foul sorcery had been the order of the day. Conventional medicine, although useless, must be better than this nonsense. *The Lancet* had been correct not even to mention this dastardly affront to scientific endeavour.

Fuming doctor now blows horn in driveway, wife summoned to help from car. Slow writhing movement to get out of car as painlessly as possible. But something wrong here. Pain almost gone. Look children, daddy is now 6 inches taller than when he left this morning; he can stand straight. Disbelieving doctor, convinced of an artifact, bends forward and back several times as if praying to house. Can move, straighten, walk, hardly any pain. It worked. *The Lancet* had after all made a mistake.

Perhaps millions should be spent researching this therapy which might lead us to save tens of millions on painkillers, muscle relaxants, days off work, hospital beds. Perhaps our editorials could start the ball rolling by at least intimating that throughout the past several thousand years probably more people have derived benefit from this therapy than from any of the 'potions' that your article refers to. Perhaps editorial writers might ask their medical colleagues how many of them have ever availed themselves of acupuncture (but will not admit it publicly). They will be as surprised at the result of this survey as I was that the therapy worked.

To some scientists, including Dr. William Tiller, acupuncture challenges the very foundations of Western physiology, casting doubt on the concept of the cell as the basic structural and functional unit of living organisms. Often quoted are the researches of the North Korean biochemist, Kim Bong-Han, who claimed to have shown that the meridians are definite colloidal channels of protoplasm going deep into the body, and existing prior to any specific organs. These channels relate to endocrine activity, and control the production of cells suitable for associated organs. Tiller conceives all disease in terms of blockages of these channels, which then favour the growth of harmful organisms. Removing the blockages by drugs is the crudest and least effective therapy: massage, needles, electronic and sonic pulses, laser energy, are all preferable if used intelligently. Certainly we know that almost any type of physical energy can disturb the stability of a colloidal solution.

Such ideas are controversial and difficult to establish. However, there is much that Western researchers can accept about acupuncture. With our present knowledge of nerve conduction and related hormone activity, there is no essential physiological objection to the idea of a needle inserted in the foot affecting one of the major internal organs of the trunk. The whole body revolves on the spinal cord; and any impulse that travels to the cord may subsequently activate electrochemical activity in quite different regions of the body.

So the concept of special life-energies is not essential to some primary level of understanding acupuncture. But by introducing the idea of meridians and chakras as the complement to nerves and hormones, we can then begin to discuss intelligently the whole psychosomatic area. The centres are linked through meridian energies; the meridians generate nerve activity; nerve activity stimulates hormone secretion; and this brings us back to psychical effects. All this is analogous to modern physics where the 'imaginary', the 'virtual', the 'anti-entity' are considered relevant, meaningful, and useful concepts that help us to continue hypothesising in causal terms.

4. Space-time Dualism

Scientific concepts of space-time energies have been built up in a piecemeal way over the last three centuries in response to observable phenomena, and they naturally represent particular rationalisations from the viewpoint of physical perception. They involve a very considerable extension of normal human vision; and we now know that many forms of radiation such as radio-waves, x-rays, and micro-waves, have the same electrical and magnetic characteristics as light waves, but different frequencies of vibration. Consequently, we also know that, were our eyes sensitive only to radio waves, we would observe a very different universe.

Because of its relation to light energy and human perception, one is inclined to classify electromagnetic energy as physical, particularly the electrical component which can be directly associated with the electron energies of the atom. Magnetic forces inevitably appear in any situation of changing electrical energy; but not having discovered a fundamental magnetic particle like the electric charge or electron, magnetic forces remain more of a mystery to the physical observer. However, relativity theory indicates that what may appear as an electrical field to one observer, may be a magnetic field to a differently moving observer.

The other two main forms of scientific energy, the inward gravitational effects, and the binding forces of the atomic nucleus – the *strong* force – are not so naturally placed in a physical category. To Newton, gravity was a mathematical necessity given the basic laws of mechanics. To the relativist, this force has almost been abstracted away by postulating that space-time structure changes in the presence of matter, and the resulting distortions generate gravitational effects. However, abstract though this is, we move into even more imaginative realms with the nuclear force: this is accounted for in terms of *virtual* energies and particles that have only a fleeting existence and momentary effect on our physical world.

As briefly discussed in chapter 2, the energy concepts of Eastern thought are more unified, and applicable to the whole phenomenal world. There is a suctional etheric energy complementing the physical and observable energies, and together they generate various

oscillatory forms. Matter and ether, in their most compressed or discrete particle forms, can be regarded as the extreme point polarities
of the two phases of akasic energy – the passive or Yin phase
of mechanistic forces and fields, and the active or Yang phase bringing order and structure to disintegrative physical tendencies. One
must however be careful about the 'passive' nature of the Yin force
because, from our normal perceptual viewpoint, this is the primary
active physical force. It is only passive in the sense that it is derived
from the Yang effect, and that it represents the more mechanical
and deterministic aspect of energy activity.

The overall effect of these oppositely polarised energies is often
expressed in inner-outer terms – a simplification that helps us to
compare Eastern and Western concepts. Energy flows from an etheric
periphery towards a centre or focus where the fundamental transformation to matter and outward physical energy takes place; subsequently, the peripheral forces direct the energy back towards the
centre. This is a bounded cyclic process, suggestive of a continuous
big-bang, with no energy lost in the overall system.

Such a view of energy dynamics is scientifically intelligible. The
solar system is conceived in terms of inward gravitational forces, the
creation of matter at the centre, and outward particle and radiation
flows. In the atom, the model is similar, with gravitation being
replaced by the cohesive nuclear force. And in organic life, we can
conceive of corresponding processes creating the cytoplasm and nucleus of the cell, or the cortex and medulla of organs. Science directly
observes the Yin aspects of the energy cycle, but can only indirectly
conceptualise the balancing and controlling Yang aspects.

These integrative energies remain central problems of science and,
working with the purely particle theories of this century, it would be
difficult to say that much fundamental progress has been made. Most
of the effort in physics has gone into trying to understand the cohesion of the atomic nucleus. The principal components of the nucleus
are protons, which have a positive electrical charge, and neutrons
that have no electrical effects. Because positive charges repel each
other, it is necessary to find some binding force to hold these units
together. Once it was thought that there must be some counteracting
negative charges within the nucleus, but this has long since been
discounted. It is certainly a most powerful force because, except for
some of the heaviest elements, the nucleus is very stable, and can
only be altered under extremely high energy conditions. And when,
under the fission of heavy elements, or the fusion of light elements,
the nucleus is altered, then immense quantities of energy are
released.

To this problem of nuclear cohesion, physicists have postulated extremely strong forces acting only within the infinitesimal domain of the nucleus, and for infinitesimal time-intervals. These are generated by particles called mesons interacting continuously with protons and neutrons. It was at one time hoped that mesons, protons, and neutrons would form a closed system of interactive energies to account for all nuclear phenomena; but the immense quantities of complex data coming in from the various accelerators have proved too difficult for such a theory. So today, physicists are trying a new conceptual approach involving smaller particles called quarks, these being held together by massless particles called gluons. However, the number and variety of these particles are growing, and there is the fundamental problem that, in the way physicists think about these things, a massless particle would have an infinite range. Already there are competing theories in the air, both of a field and particle nature.

In modern theorising, the notion of the *anti-particle* is as fundamental as that of the particle. An anti-particle has opposite electrical and magnetic polarities, but the same mass as a corresponding particle. Its existence in the observable physical world is inevitably very short-lived, for on meeting a complementary particle, mass in the classical sense is annihilated, and the energy of both entities is transformed into electromagnetic radiation precisely according to $E = mc^2$. Thus, in the material world, which seems to have an unbounded supply of normal particles, the anti-particle has no chance of surviving for more than a fraction of a second. This has led physicists to speculate that there might be in other parts of the universe anti-worlds consisting of anti-matter constructed purely from anti-particles.

Thinking along different lines, Paul Dirac, as mentioned previously, thought of space as a boundless ocean of aetheric electrons of negative mass, with the positrons, or anti-electrons, as gaps or holes in this aether created when the negative-mass particles were forced up into the positive-mass state of normal electrons. Such negative mass-energy, although ignored, is allowed for in modern physics according to the relativistic formula

$$E^2 = M^2c^4 + p^2c^2$$

where M is the mass of the particle at rest, and 'p' its momentum. If the particle is at rest, the formula gives not only that $E = Mc^2$, but also that $E = -Mc^2$. In the Dirac formulation, we note that the aetheric electron has negative mass and negative charge; the positron has positive mass and positive charge; and the normal electron has positive mass and negative charge.

Thus, Dirac conceived the particle world as having energy levels, either beginning on the positive side with minimum value Mc^2, going up indefinitely as the momentum increased; or beginning at $-Mc^2$, going down to a negative infinity.

Complementing this picture of particle energy levels are the energy levels of a unit of radiation – a photon, whose rest-mass is zero. The formula used by physicists here is that $E = hf$, where 'f' is the frequency, and 'h' is a universal constant named after Planck, one of the founders of quantum theory which expresses the idea that radiation is propagated and transferred to matter in discrete energy packets. As a by-product of Planck's formula, we would note in passing that, as photons travel through space with a velocity of 'c', their actual mass 'm' is deduced from $E = hf = mc^2$; therefore $m = hf/c^2$.

These photon levels, increasing with frequency, constitute the electromagnetic radiation spectrum (figure 4.1), which can be thought of as a piano keyboard of about 80 octaves. In this, the visual spectrum

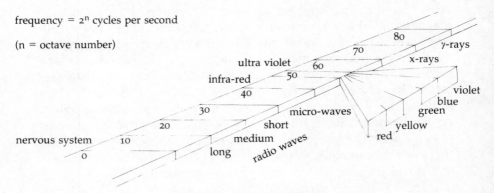

Fig. 4.1   Electromagnetic spectrum

occupies just one octave, and each of the main colours about one tone within the octave (an octave being an interval in which the frequency is doubled from bottom to top note).

The concept of light as a particular waveband of electromagnetic energy was developed, and put into definite mathematical form by Clerk Maxwell just over a hundred years ago. His famous equations, the Maxwell equations, cover all the main aspects of electrical and magnetic activity, and are based on continuous aetheric fields rather than discrete energy quanta like photons. Magnets, charges, and currents were conceived as creating disturbances in an aetheric ocean, and, on an inverse square law basis, they affected other material sources of electromagnetic energy. His equations are still extensively used in technology, and are even compatible with relativistic ideas.

The equations embody one of the most impressive theories of science, comparable even to Newtonian mechanics and gravitational theory. In fact, when the older gravitational ideas are expressed in field form, the equations generated are very similar in appearance to those of Maxwell.

Using modern quantum ideas, which are essentially geared to high-energy particle phenomena, we lose sight of important aspects of electromagnetism. Maxwell's equations, which deal with high and low frequencies, with static and non-periodic effects, make very clear a certain complementarity, or dualism, in electric and magnetic vectors with respect to space and time. Taking the simplest form of the equations for a wave in free space, they give

$$\frac{\partial E}{\partial x} = -\frac{1}{c}\frac{\partial H}{\partial t}; \quad \frac{\partial H}{\partial y} = -\frac{1}{c}\frac{\partial E}{\partial t}$$

This says that the rate of change of one vector *with respect to space* is proportional to the rate of change of the other *with respect to time*. And solving the equations, we get the following *plane polarised* waveforms (figure 4.2).

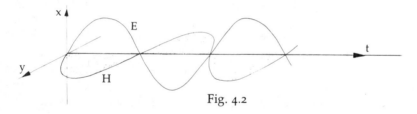
Fig. 4.2

With a slightly more complex form of the equations, we get the interesting *circularly polarised* waveform (figure 4.3) in which the electric and magnetic vectors generate complementary chains of a double helix.

Classical electromagnetics was based on concepts of positive and negative charges, and north and south poles. However, as positive

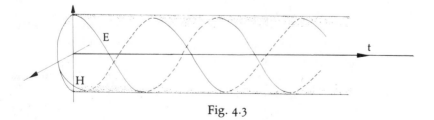
Fig. 4.3

electricity came to be thought of as a deficiency of electrons, and no evidence could be found for the single isolated magnetic pole, modern physics has concentrated on electron activity in the atom as the only source of electromagnetism. The charge of the electron gives rise to electrical forces, and its *spin* produces magnetic effects. This latter idea can be associated with the electric-magnetic relationships shown below (figure 4.4), these representing something rather more general than the previous waveform diagrams.

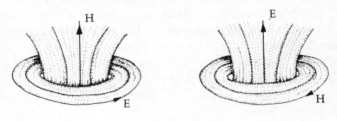

Fig. 4.4

In today's theorising, all particles have certain basic parameters, or quantum numbers, of which mass, and charge, and spin are the most fundamental; and all forces are derived from the various energy quanta associated with atomic structure. Maxwell's aether could not be conceptualised in positive mass-energy terms, and so we are left just with positive-mass particles interacting in an empty space. Gravitational forces do not form part of this scheme of things, although the term *graviton* is sometimes used as the fundamental unit on the assumption of incorporation into quantum ideas one day. In theoretical work, gravitation comes under the General Theory of Relativity; but in practical terms, Newtonian gravitation, and its nineteenth century field version, is the basis of almost all calculation. Those scientific historians who would have us believe that we have thrown out classical electromagnetics and Newtonian ideas in favour of quantum theory and Relativity, seem not to be aware of the inapplicability of many modern theories because of the impossible mathematics they throw up, leaving most scientists and technologists still completely dependent on older ideas.

The three main categories of energy in modern physics – electromagnetism, the nuclear force, and gravity – are understood well enough to develop some specialised technologies. But there is a tendency to claim far too much for our limited level of understanding. The most obvious area of ignorance is in structural matters. There are useful theories about how atoms in molecules are held together by residual electrical forces, but beyond this it becomes very conjectural. One would expect, for example, that modern theory would allow us to design and synthesise new materials to precise specifications, but in fact we still rely on trial and error methods.

If negative mass-energy exists, it would have cohesive and structuring properties, drawing in positive mass-energies, either particles or radiation. And for this reason, it would be unobservable, because physical observation depends on reflected or non-absorbed energies. With a negative-energy aether replacing the empty space of modern physics, and negative energy forms complementing and controlling physical development, there would be definite possibilities of new structural understandings. The black-hole concept of cosmology is a step in this direction. When a star collapses, and the inner-outer energy balance can no longer be sustained, all energy may ultimately be directed inwards, so creating a suctional domain with negative mass and time characteristics.

Dr William Tiller, referred to in the previous chapter, considers that, while electrical effects correspond essentially to physical processes, magnetic fields are characteristics of a reverse-time, etheric space, whose negative energy brings order and cohesion to the physical. He further suggests that when particles approach the velocity of light, they then tunnel through the energy barrier to be transformed into etheric particles with a large negative energy. This implies a continuous cycle of energy between physical and etheric spaces in terms analogous to those described in chapter 2.

Léon Brillouin, the distinguished French physicist, has suggested that if we allow for a continuous spectrum of positive and negative energy levels, then it should be possible to formulate a straightforward theory of inward gravitational radiation very similar to Maxwell's theory for the outward electromagnetic energy. Brillouin finds Einstein's theory of gravitation so over-generalised, as well as quite unreconciled to the electromagnetic world. Moreover, it does not even provide the experimental physicist with a practical idea of length and time, while evidence in support is so meagre after over fifty years of effort, and not too convincing at that. He suggests that the little evidence that has been put forward can be explained in far simpler terms. For instance, the bending of light rays near the sun does not have to depend on curved space, but can be rationalised in terms of the sun's gravitational effect on light photons (of mass-energy hf/c^2 as previously shown), together with a small reduction of the velocity of light near the sun.

To make gravitational theory compatible with classical electromagnetics, Brillouin has had to invent a second gravitational vector for correspondence with the electric and magnetic vectors. Then, using the classical formula for field density, he goes on to show that any spherical positive mass must be enveloped by a negative energy domain. Here again, we have some correspondence with esoteric ideas.

However the second gravitational vector seems arbitrary. If some new energy theory is going to be developed along these lines, then perhaps we should be thinking about 'gravimagnetics' to complement electromagnetics, with the magnetic field as the link, or the common denominator, between the electrical and the gravitational. As Dirac has pointed out, our energy theories could have been developed from the magnetic monopole rather than from the electric charge.

Another approach has recently been put forward by Harold Aspden. Returning to the beginning of the century, and rejecting special relativity, he develops the concept of a quantised aether containing a fine lattice of energy quanta from which the physical particles are derived, and through which the forces of electromagnetism and gravitation are mediated. Starting from an analysis of forces between moving electrons (electrodynamics), he obtains not only the main twentieth century formulae, but also calculates the universal constant of gravitation – thus seeming to unify gravitation and electromagnetism. The formula $E = mc^2$ he derives from Newton and Maxwell; and concerning the contentious Michelson-Morley experiment, he points out that, with the modern laser experiments, the Doppler effect gives the precise correction required.

This is a very bold thesis, and far too revolutionary for most physicists. But for those technologically inclined, this concept of a structured space may have important implications. Harold Aspden discusses, for instance, the curious rotational energies of ball-lightning, whose almost lifelike properties are an enigma to orthodox physics – just what sustains it, and gives it coherence? A quantised aether with specific rotational properties does give an explanation.

Nikola Tesla, the Yugoslav physicist, and one of the most original people in the whole history of science, showed at the turn of the century how to generate ball-lightning from electromagnetic coils. This was just one of a myriad of discoveries and inventions, which included demonstrating to the whole world how to generate, transmit, and use alternating-current on the large scale. He eventually came to the conclusion that electricity could be generated at almost no cost by suitable resonance with the earth's aether. After half a century of neglect, his work is now being looked at again seriously. Some are hoping that ball-lightning will provide the necessary containment properties for nuclear fusion; others are trying to tap the earth's field. Modern physics provides little guidance in these matters, but Aspden's aetheric theory may indicate a way forward.

Compared with the end of the last century, the current energy concepts present a confusing picture, obscuring many ideas of significance, and making for difficulties where once there seemed more clarity. For instance, dropping the concept of the all-pervading aether has meant that field effects on a particle had to be replaced by subatomic interactions. Thus, what was once a simple electrostatic field between two charges is now a continuous exchange of photons. Yet at the same time as disposing of the electromagnetic aether, we are encouraged to think of gravitation in terms of geometrical distortions of a space-time continuum.

One wonders how much present difficulties are the result of particular conceptual fashions and modes of expression. While the new physics is partly the trial and error response to the complex experimental data coming from ever more powerful and sophisticated equipment, it is partly also an aesthetic response. The relativistic idea, for instance, that all phenomena and equations must appear the same to all observers moving at uniform relative velocities is based on a feeling about the way things ought to be, rather than on experimental evidence. In fact, the few replications of the Michelson-Morley experiment attempted have never given absolutely conclusive answers one way or another. Like everything else, physics is dominated by particular personalities (most very ignorant of physiology); and it is sometimes their emotional pull as much as their rationality that may finally win the day in competing theories.

But out of the present complexities is slowly emerging something more fundamental than the energy polarities inherited from classical physics. What we are now trying to grasp and conceptualise is the basic duality between the outgoing mechanistic forces representing the physical side of life, and the structural integrative forces concerned with the development of living forms. When one looks at the difficulties of physics and physiology, it takes little imagination to conceive of a resolving and unifying theme involving two separate, yet interactive spaces – a theme that like Elgar's enigma, pervades everything, but is never explicitly stated.

In the process of categorisation into two complementary sets of forces based on positive and negative mass-energies, one would hope to remove many of the artificial rules that have had to be constructed to force all phenomena into a (3–1) asymmetrical space-time frame of reference, involving an ever-increasing series of quantum characteristics like *colour* and *charm* and *strangeness*. In place of the fearful complexities of nuclear and space-time theory, we can rather more simply conceive of suctional energies integrating the atomic nuclei, with gravitation perhaps as some residual effect – this being such an infinitesimal force at the atomic level. And between the atomic and cosmic extreme, and underlying the electrochemical activity of the body, we can envisage a range of oscillatory Yin-Yang processes that develop and sustain organic forms.

But probably the most important aspect of such a rationalisation is why different energy plus and minuses of electric charges and magnetic poles do not simply cancel each other out, and bring the universe to an immediate end. It is not a simple minus sign that distinguishes mathematically physical and non-physical quantities, but rather the imaginary number 'i'. This entity is entering into every aspect of particle physics in the mathematical attempts to make some causal sense of subatomic interactions. The concept of the virtual particle, for instance, which has to fill strange gaps between disjointed physical effects is continuously appealed to in everyday work. There is a new *imaginary* inner world developing in physics that seems to exist in its own right, and yet is complementary to all *real* phenomena of the observable physical world. Real and imaginary, physical and etheric, '1' and 'i' cannot be further reduced in their primitive forms, and therefore cannot eliminate each other. Only in derived forms, such as in quantitative energy functions, can they relate directly.

To the mathematician, the importance of complex entities with real and imaginary components has long been recognised. In the classical electromagnetics of Clerk Maxwell, for instance, it is often possible to manipulate electric and magnetic fields together in complex functions, and then separate them out through the real and imaginary aspects. It is also used extensively in problems of rotation, including Newtonian dynamics of spinning bodies. This can be linked to the idea that, as the number -1 implies a reversal of direction, and as $i \times i = -1$, then operating with a single 'i' represents half this rotation, or a vector at right angles to the original.

In relativity theory, the operator 'i' is used in the definition of the time-dimension, and the working out of a 4-dimensional geometry. The basic 'interval' expression between two events is given by $s^2 - c^2t^2$, where 's' is the 3-dimensional distance, 'c' the velocity of light, and 't' the time. By defining a new fourth-dimensional term 'T', equal to 'ict', the interval becomes $s^2 + T^2$, i.e. symmetrical in distance and time parameters, although still dimensionally asymmetrical. If we choose 'c' to be unity, then the 4-dimensional continuum can be expressed simply as (s,it).

But the most far-reaching aspect of complex number forms is that they allow us to manipulate functions in an all-embracing totality in which there are no exceptions, and everything is allowed for. In geometry, this totality is termed the Complex Projective Space where real and imaginary elements have the same status. In this closed continuum, a line will always intersect another line or curve, whether at real, or imaginary, or complex, or infinite points. Visualisation of results in this space can be exceedingly bizarre with, for instance, the centre of a circle appearing outside the circumference. But with the right geometrical attitudes, this is no problem. One comes to perceive, in the overall homogeneity and economy of the approach, an unusual beauty and power.

This Projective Geometry is a branch of mathematics brought to fruition at the end of the last century, but is now sadly neglected by our schools and universities, it having no natural part to play in the materialist scheme of things. It has its origins in Greek geometry which recognised that all the conic forms of circle, ellipse, parabola, and hyperbola, could be derived from differently angled sections of a cone, and that the theorems about one curve could be projected through the cone onto another curve, giving corresponding relationships. This projection concept suggested a way of developing geometrical knowledge without the artifice of dimensional axes, and with little reference to metric quantities. In this, and in the fact that our perspective pictures are created by conical projection, it would seem more relevant to visual perception than any other form of geometry.

In the evolution of this geometry, the specifically 'projective' aspect has largely disappeared, and been replaced by general ideas of (1–1) correspondence between point and line. Every line is generated by a set of related points, and every point by a set of related lines passing through the point. Related pencils of lines generate curves, and related sets of points generate tangents enveloping curves. This complementary way of thinking about points, lines, and curves, leads to the powerful conclusion that every geometrical form, and the relationships contained within it, can be turned inside out into a *dual* form with corresponding relationships. Thus, there is a reversal of perception between dual entities, yet retaining a fundamental consistency about each relationship.

In practical terms, it is not difficult to get some space-time sense of this geometrical duality. If we were to move away from the earth at the speed of light, then light photons would appear in a static point-like way, and material energies would give the impression of energy rays receding from us. Perception would thus be reversed, with particles and rays, points and lines, being inverted, so giving us a complementary view of the universe.

This geometrical duality is beautifully illustrated in the diagrams below (figure 4.5) in which a theorem of Brianchon is turned inside out to give us the famous *mystic hexagram* of Pascal. Thus the six tangents generating the rays p, q, r that converge on the internal point X are transformed, through the dualising process, into six points on the conic, generating in turn the points P, Q, R lying on the external ray x.

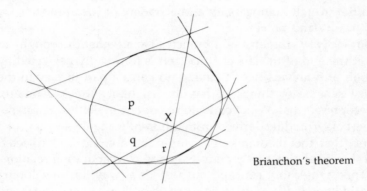

Brianchon's theorem

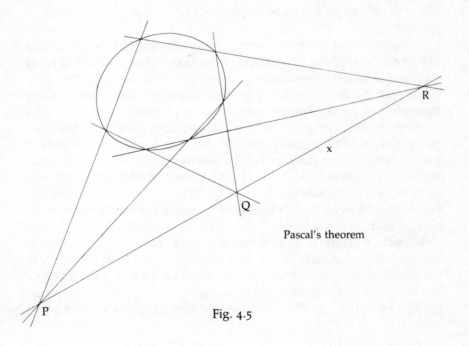

Pascal's theorem

Fig. 4.5

In the real physical world of 3-dimensional space, duality of this nature is still valid, but takes a rather more complex form. The basic elements of this space are the point, line, and plane; and in the 3-dimensional duality, the point transforms to the plane, the plane to the point, and the line, being the join of points or intersection of planes, is self-dual, or corresponds to itself. The theorems shown have their natural equivalences in three dimensions, with, for instance, external tangential planes generating the internal point X. By means of such a geometry, George Adams, who tried to follow up some of the Steiner ideas in geometrical terms, considered that we would come to understand the fashioning of organic forms – not through inner molecular processes, but through peripheral planar forces acting inwards on matter, and moulding it like a potter or sculptor.

There are a number of interesting ways of developing this geometry, the most elegant of which is based on general theorems of correspondence which largely avoid algebraic notation. However, by developing it in terms of real and imaginary numbers, the associations with space-time energy and perceptual problems are much more evident.

Working on these lines, the basic premise for a geometrical-perceptual duality is very simply derived. A single physical point can be regarded as a circle of zero radius. A normal circle of radius 'r' is defined by the Pythagoras statement of $x^2 + y^2 = r^2$; and if the radius is reduced to zero, this becomes the point-circle

$$x^2 = -y^2 \quad \text{or} \quad x = \pm iy$$

Thus, a physical point can be regarded as the point of intersection of two non-physical lines. This is the starting-point of geometrical duality, leading to the general idea that each point-line physical representation has its non-physical line-point correlate – as shown in the Pascal and Brianchon theorems.

Proceeding just a little further with this approach, there are two very fundamental points in projective geometry called the *circular points at infinity* which are of great importance in relating general projective theorems to the simpler physical Euclidean geometry. These are 'infinite complex' points through which all circles, however large or small, pass. To introduce infinite points, one has to write the point (x, y) as $[(x/t), (y/t)]$, and then subsequently put $t = 0$. For notational convenience, we then talk about the point (x, y, t), where, for non-infinite points, 't' can be regarded as 1. The reader should then be able to see that the points $(1, i, 0)$ and $(1, -i, 0)$ always satisfy the circle $x^2 + y^2 = r^2 t^2$.

Thus we have a most interesting geometrical situation. The point circle is both a point, and two imaginary straight lines; and moreover, these lines contain the circular points at infinity which, by definition, lie on the original point-circle. The physical point is therefore in some sense 'coincident' with two non-physical points at infinity. Or in somewhat more sophisticated terms, we might say that the non-physical rays generate the physical point, with the infinity of one space transforming to the zero of the other.

Thus the original point-circle may be conceived with symbolic coordinates as shown below (figure 4.6). A is the physical point, CA and BA the non-physical lines, and BC the 'line at infinity'. The arrows of this *perceptual triangle* suggest a possible circuit of energy akin to the physical-etheric model, with transformations, governed by the operator 'i', at the physical point A, and along the etheric periphery BC.

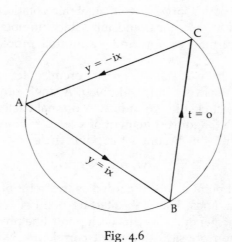

Fig. 4.6

With the notation we have used, it is tempting to regard 't' as in some way representing time. Then in our perception-triangle, AB indicates positive or forwards time, CA negative or reverse time, and BC (t = 0) is timeless.

These are the three basic categories of time to be found in most esoteric literature: the highest cosmic or spiritual levels are said to be timeless, while physical and lower etheric levels give us the positive and negative time-polarities. Science, too, has recently accepted these categories: anti-particles and black-holes are theorised about in terms of negative-time; while relativity indicates an approach to the timeless as particles move towards the speed of light. In fact, of course, if 't' is assumed to be a scalar or one-dimensional entity, these are the only algebraic alternatives. Thus we find mysticism and mathematical-physics surprisingly consistent with one another.

In Newton's day, things were much simpler. Time was something unique and absolute for the whole universe. It was essentially independent of space, or the measurement of space. There was the external sense of uniform time in the movements of the heavenly bodies consistent with our own time devices here on earth. Using this commonsense view, Newton was able to move forward from a static geometry and mechanics to the dynamical methods of the calculus and the study of motion. Fortunately, he did not get bogged down with the problems of how one measures space with light waves from a moving origin, and difficulties about simultaneity for differently moving observers – had he done so, he would have made little progress. He simply used his own innate sense and experience about the nature of both time and space, and in a few years, made more progress in physical calculation and prediction than has ever been made before or since.

Since the Einstein school proposed a relativity of time between differently moving observers, and also that the concept of 'simultaneity' that had always been taken for granted, was no longer valid, time has become mystical and esoteric in the best Eastern tradition. If one person's time unit is faster than another's, then this suggests that the future of one is apparent to the other. However, this difficulty has been theoretically avoided by ensuring that it would not be possible to communicate the future of one to the other because of the laws governing electromagnetic transfers of information. In this, the physicist differs from the mystic who maintains one can enter timeless and reverse-time states while still retaining physical awareness.

But it is one thing to postulate various time possibilities through equations; it is quite another to relate them to the subjective experience of time. Can people, for example, delay the ageing processes through very fast space travel, or is this just a relativity of perception, with the space travellers experiencing within themselves the same ageing rates? In times of intense activity, in times of waiting, in sleep, or in love, we are aware of great variations in the conscious experience of time – how does this fit into nice neat equations about x, y, z, and t, and tidy theories of energy flow? Such problems have been argued over interminably this century, but with few conclusions. One wonders whether to agree with the view that time itself is the great illusion.

The Special Theory of Relativity does at least move us on to some more flexible view of the time-dimension. In fact, if we express space-time in the simple dual form of (s, it), we can regard this as two complementary entities that can be experienced either from the 'real' or 'imaginary' side. In other words, 's' is the external perception of space, while 't' is the complementary internal experience that, in waking consciousness, involves the time-sense.

If we operate on this with 'i', we get

$$(is, i^2t) \quad or \quad (is, -t)$$

Thus the 'real' part is now a reverse-time world. Moreover, $E = mc^2$ is transformed to $E = m(ic)^2$, bringing us back to $E = -mc^2$ for the mass-energy effect of counter-space.

This transformation is completely in line with the geometrical concept of the Complex Projective Space, which incorporates two complementary perceptual worlds, with 'i' as the fundamental notational entity relating one form to the other. And in the geometrical dualising operations between real and imaginary aspects, one is in effect making the perceptual changes analogous to space and time. In human terms, this means that the external experience of physical space, and the internal experience of the counter-space that is characterised by the time-sense in normal life, can be turned inside out, and the inner psychical world viewed objectively. It also gives substance to the thought that every point of space contains all of time, and every point of time contains all of space.

Time, in the scientific sense, could be thought of as some interactive vibrational parameter between the two spaces – as indicated by the measurement of time through atomic vibration. Using this limited physical concept of time, we can say that the transformed perceptual world is characterised by negative mass-energy and reverse-time. It should be noted that anti-particles do not fit both criteria: they have, according to the rationalisations of modern physics, positive mass-energy and negative-time characteristics. Therefore they must represent some intermediate phenomena between the two spaces – this also being suggested by Dirac's original argument for the existence of the anti-electron or positron.

A possible way of further developing this line of thought is through the *quaternion* algebra of the distinguished Irish mathematician, Sir William Hamilton. For many years he had tried, without success, to generalise the essentially 2-dimensional algebra of real-imaginary number-pairs into a three-dimensional form consisting of a real number and two distinct types of imaginary numbers. But one day, while walking along the bank of the Royal Canal near Dublin, 'the galvanic circuit of thought closed' when he suddenly realised that he needed a fourfold term with three imaginary entities i, j, and k; and the following basic relationships he inscribed there and then on a bridge:

$$i^2 = j^2 = k^2 = ijk = -1$$

Thus we have three distinct roots of -1; and with the further relationship that $ij = k$, they satisfy the basic condition for three perpendicular vectors, so constituting an alternative set of axes.

However, as with the duality of Projective Geometry, applied scientists could discover little natural use for Hamilton's quaternions – although by ignoring the real part, and taking the imaginary aspects as representing a normal 3-dimensional vector, the quaternion algebra reduces to the vector algebra that is extensively used in all mathematical physics. Maxwell tried to use the quaternions in their original form, but complained that one was always correcting the minus sign for such inherently positive functions as kinetic energy. However, it seems possible that Hamilton's three rotational operators may provide us with a natural notation for developing a mathematical understanding of the counter-space – perhaps to be expressed in the form (ix, jy, kz).

This particular form of the counter-space does in fact allow us to generalise to three dimensions the previous ideas discussed about points, lines, and circles of 2-dimensional projective geometry. The point-sphere, for example, can be described in terms of the imaginary planes in the form

$$ix \pm jy \pm kz = 0$$

These may be regarded as the imaginary 'generators' of the sphere – or in the terminology of George Adams, the formative etheric planes. Thus, instead of describing them by this most misunderstood word 'imaginary', we might more appropriately and sensibly refer to them as *imaging* planes.

In rotational terms, the imaging axes of the counter-space represent rotations through $90°$ of the real axes of physical space – this giving a different slant on imaging in the sense of mirror-image, or right and left-handed forms as found in particle physics and molecular chemistry.

One other most important aspect comes out of this formulation. In the physical space, the distance term 's' is given by

$$s = \sqrt{x^2 + y^2 + z^2}$$

Performing the same operation on the counter-space, we obtain a 'distance' term of the form

$$i\sqrt{x^2 + y^2 + z^2}$$

Equating this to the 'it' term used in modern physics, this would indicate that 'time' as we experience it is a measure of distance in the counter-space. Movement forward in time, regression through time, and timelessness, then all have a natural interpretation in the counter-space, and may be thought of in terms of psychical or psychological movement.

Such a formulation involving two complementary subspaces is something beyond classical and relativistic ideas. It does not invalidate what has been done in the development of space-time concepts based on material forms, but it opens up more possibilities. For example, when theorising about mental communication, scientific hypotheses inevitably are based on electromagnetic modes of transfers of information. But subconscious communication between individuals, such as was demonstrated so convincingly by Edgar Cayce, does not seem to have these physical space-time constraints. There would appear to be inner channels of energy distinct from electromagnetics, with the subconscious having immediate access to particular etheric forms and effects, regardless of space and time differences. This we can understand in general terms through the mathematics of space and counter-space; and such understanding should lead on to specific experimentation, in contrast to the present hit and miss methods now associated with ESP research.

Over the last few years, there has certainly been a move amongst mathematicians towards higher-dimensional spaces, with the 4-dimensional continuum of relativity being regarded as a particular projection of the higher space. In this work, there is always the danger of over-generalisation and abstraction far removed from our living world. What is being proposed here is that the two separate, yet interactive domains of outer and inner space represent the totality of the evolving phenomenal world of mind and matter. Beyond this, there may well be a timeless spiritual domain of pure consciousness – beyond the mind, beyond all dualities, and beyond all activity and change and desire. To some, this represents the ultimate goal of enlightenment; to others, it is ultimate nothingness and extinction. Whatever it is, it is beyond our living phenomenal world, and therefore beyond all causal knowledge.

5. Biofield Concepts

Compared with the subatomic and cosmic problems that most physicists devote their time to, the energies and forces of organic life would seem to be of an entirely different order of complexity. Observing the miraculous development of the embryo, we soon realise that physicists are dealing with the easier problems, however fearsome they now appear to be.

In this chapter, we will develop some tentative ideas about biofields, and their possible relevance to organic structure and function. And as introductory to this subject, we will consider some patterning effects of rotational motion. In a sense, this may be regarded as an interpolation from the idea of 'spin' in particle physics. All rotational motion of course represents energy, and when the rotation has a consistent frequency or spin, then there is a measure of cohesion or stability. In fact, we could say that any specific rotational pattern has a certain independent 'identity' distinct from the background continuum. The energy quanta of subatomic physics, for instance, can be regarded as 'particles' in this sense. Quite possibly, the rotational and frequency aspects of these particles determine all their energy characteristics. And it may be that the field effects of the spin, that we call magnetism, form the basis of all energy phenomena.

My own first specific ideas about biofields came from a little consideration of the chakral patterns. Although very unlikely to impress the academic mind, it may be helpful to sketch briefly the origin of some of the more sophisticated ideas coming later in the book. As previously described, the seven rotational centres along the cerebro-spinal axis are perceived as the major areas of physical-psychical interaction, with different energy patterns regulating and balancing particular functions of the neuroendocrine system. Cosmic or magnetic energies are considered to be sucked into the centre of each vortex, and then to radiate outwards like the spokes of a revolving wheel.

In both the Yoga and acupuncture traditions, gradations of energy level are important, each level having its own specific effects on the energy centres and internal organs. From lowest prana to highest akasa, or from absolute Yin to absolute Yang, there are considered to be six, or eight, or twelve significant levels of energy controlling different cell and tissue formations.

In Western physics, energy level is often synonymous with frequency, and all material structures have their own resonant frequencies to which they most readily respond. So, assuming the chakral perceptions have some objective validity, one's first tentative guess about the patterns is that the number of divisions, or petals, may give some indication of relative frequency. From the root to the crown, the older texts give the following numerical sequence:

$$4 \quad 6 \quad 10 \quad 12 \quad 16 \quad 2 \quad 1000$$

and more modern versions give

$$4 \quad 6 \quad 10 \quad 12 \quad 16 \quad 96 \quad 960/12$$

Remembering that a doubling of frequency represents an octave, then this would give a two-octave span for the trunk. More specifically, if the lowest centre is represented by the note C, then the other trunk centres would be G, E, G, C, and so constitute the most natural form of the tonic chord as used at the beginning and end of classical musical sequences. In this chord, all is resolved; and one can go on to argue that all other chords (non-tonic ones) do not find natural resonance within the psyche, producing instead varying degrees of tension or stimulation between the centres. Also we might note that other versions of the tonic chord having a different bass note, or without a third, or the third repeated, leave something to be desired. All of which, to musical people at least, makes quite a convincing argument for the relative-frequency interpretation of the chakral divisions.

However, first thoughts are often naive thoughts leading to nothing in particular. To make a little progress, we need to look at the patterns with a more geometrical mind (figure 5.1). Those with some familiarity of spirographs will know that the lotus patterns can be produced when one rotation is superimposed on another. It is very easy to understand the reason for this. At certain angles of radius, the rotations merge and reinforce each other. At other angles, they tend to cancel each other out. Thus around the circumference of the rotation, the overall pattern oscillates inwards and outwards, so creating distinctive divisions.

One can sometimes see these patterns in a most spectacular way when the propeller blades of a hovercraft slow down, and rotate with different frequencies. Very distinctive lotus patterns can be observed if one is in the right position. According to frequency or rate of rota-

Chakral patterns
(Leadbeater)

Fig. 5.1

tion, and to the direction of rotation, the petals will be wide or narrow; and in general, the number of petals will be related to the algebraic difference of frequency.

Developing this line of thought a little by means of the simplest possible model consisting of two rotating radii, certain things become immediately apparent. First to be noted is that if the two rotation rates are exactly equal and opposite, then the vectors will come together at two diametrically opposite points. But if there were just a small difference in frequency, they would converge a little off centre and, over a number of revolutions, many distinct divisions of the circle would be generated. For the brow centre, if there are 96 divisions rather than 2, this could be accounted for by two closely-tuned oscillators with frequency ratio 47 : 49.

Thus on this line of reasoning, the original numbers associated with the brow and crown centres would not necessarily be any indication of relative frequency, particularly if we are considering opposite rotations. Very high numbers may indicate very small differences in frequency – although lower numbers could give some approximation of relative frequency. Given the number of lotus divisions, there does not exist a unique pair of frequencies to produce this effect. There are many possibilities and different solutions according to the direction of rotation. For instance, a 4-petalled form could be generated by opposite rotations with 3 : 1 frequency ratio, or by rotations in the same direction of 5 : 1 and 7 : 3. With the 6-petalled form of the female centre, there is the interesting possibility that this could also be a 5 : 1 frequency ratio, only with reverse rotations. Similarly stomach and heart centres can both be represented by a 11 : 1 ratio.

So we cannot from the lotus divisions alone determine precise relative frequencies. However, we would be inclined to eliminate certain ratios by taking into account the individual petal forms of figure 5.1. Clearly figure 5.2 indicates that a 11 : 1 ratio is to be preferred to a 7 : 5 ratio. And doing this for all the trunk centres, we might reach the tentative conclusion of opposite rotations, and ratios

$$3:1 \quad 5:1 \quad 9:1 \quad 11:1 \quad 15:1$$

for the five forms. This would imply one fundamental note, together with relative frequencies 3 : 5 : 9 : 11 : 15 spanning just over two octaves.

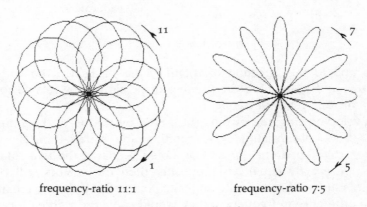

frequency-ratio 11:1   frequency-ratio 7:5

Fig. 5.2   12-petalled forms

Alternatively, looking at figure 5.3, a 7 : 1 ratio with similar rotations seems preferable to 5 : 1. Thus, conjecturing that adjacent centres are oppositely polarised with respect to the direction of rotation, the ratio sequence 3 : 7 : 9 : 13 : 15 is another possibility. Such thoughts can be kept in the back of the mind when we consider spinal frequencies later in the book from more modern viewpoints.

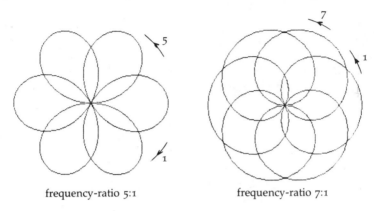

frequency-ratio 5:1   frequency-ratio 7:1

Fig. 5.3   6-petalled forms

In the cerebral area, there is reason to think that the complementary aspects of the cortex, and the two eyes, indicate oppositely polarised structuring forces and opposite rotations. From an endocrine point of view, there are two distinct aspects of the pituitary: the *anterior* developing upwards from the roof of the mouth, and the *posterior* developing downwards from the hypothalamus. Thus with the symmetrically placed pineal behind and above the two frontal centres, we might begin to understand the brow and crown patterns in terms of three oscillatory centres with comparatively small difference frequencies, and opposite rotations between the frontal centres. This concept will be developed later in the book, and related to EEG evidence.

With similar rotations and large difference frequency, the effect is much the same as with opposite rotations. However, if the frequency ratio is nearly unity, then something basically different is generated. In successive rotations, the two components begin to cancel each other out, and the resultant vector spirals in towards the centre. Then subsequently, as they begin to reinforce each other, the vector spirals out towards the periphery. So we have a vortex movement, alternatively converging on, and diverging from the nuclear position.

Thus these forms, generated very simply from two rotating vectors with different frequencies or rates of rotation, give some substance to certain vague ideas about inner-outer energy flows creating chakral patterns. The actual form produced is a function of frequency-ratio and direction of rotation. With the 2-dimensional forms discussed, it is helpful to keep in mind three basic movements (figure 5.4).

1. If there is a large frequency-ratio, whether similar or opposite rotations, then lotus forms with relatively indistinct petal divisions are generated.

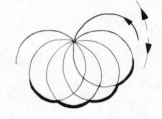

2. If the rotations are opposite, and the frequency-ratio near to unity (such as with a semitone interval), then we obtain very distinctive petal formations.

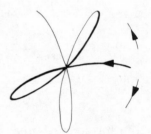

3. Where the rotations are similar, and the frequency-ratio near to unity, vortex motion is produced.

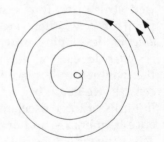

Fig. 5.4

In all cases, there is a continual inner-outer movement.

Such spiralling, vortical, and lotus forms are physically evident in plant and primitive organic life. But in the vertebrates, with their far more complex structures, one can only indirectly envisage the underlying vibrational organisation.

These structural ideas perhaps have something in common with the theories of Wilhelm Reich – a much maligned man in his time, and like Mesmer, gradually ostracised from the medical and scientific establishments. Opposing the mechanistic trend in biology, he claimed to have discovered a universal *orgone* energy which was the source of life, vitality, and above all, of sexuality. The individual unit of this bioenergy he called the *bion*, and he maintained that bions could be stored in special accumulators, and used to help cancer patients. By sitting in a very dark room, Reich tells us he and his colleagues were able to observe directly this form of energy. He described the spiral patterns of orgone, and the unique petal shape of the individual bion, in much the way just discussed. Not that Reich would have recognised any such connection, for he was rather contemptuous of Indian ideas.

Reich's biofield theories continue to interest therapists of the alternative medical schools. And such ideas have been significantly reinforced by the studies of Harold Burr, a Yale professor, who for forty years investigated electrical effects in seeds, plants, embryos, and humans using sensitive instrumentation to measure the electrical potential near the organic surface, and independent of any local current or impedance effects. Changes in potential related to major biological processes like ovulation, or to major disturbances like tumour growth. Some rhythmic activity he was able to relate to planetary cycles. Being a relatively constant field, and reflecting just the overall changes of the organism, it has been described as 'quasi-electrostatic'. As such, we can for instance understand how our electrical environment of ionised particles in the atmosphere can have a significant effect on our well-being – and this may in fact be what Reich's orgone boxes for cancer treatment were all about. Because of these, Reich spent the last months of his life in prison.

In line with genetic theory, Harold Burr found that similar seeds with just one different gene possessed very different fields. He also found that the field of the developing embryo was very stable from the earliest stages of growth. With chick embryos, he made the interesting observation that their orientation could be controlled by a simple horseshoe magnet.

His work into what he called L-fields was limited to rather static aspects, and did not involve frequency measurement – his equipment not being designed for this. Nor did he have the instrumentation to measure the magnetic component. Nevertheless it was a beginning, and his research has helped to transform the vague abstraction of a morphogenetic field into an objective and measurable energy pattern. The evidence led him neither to the orthodox scientific view that the field is simply the product of atomic and molecular activity, nor to the esoteric one that it completely controls all physical development.

His pragmatic viewpoint was that matter and field were mutually interdependent, with matter influencing field, and field influencing matter.

Following Reich, the main thrust in bioenergetics has been in cancer research. Cancer cells are those that fail to work in an integrated way. They appear to assume a life of their own, without reference to their communal functions. After the almost complete failure during the last decade of the most massive medical research programme in history into these problems, there should now be more interest in those working on a biofield basis. Theorising in these terms, we can envisage that certain cerebrospinal centres become under-active, or simply fail to function. As a consequence, the biofields are lacking vital frequencies necessary for correct cellular and chromosomal replication. On this basis, the essence of any effective form of cancer therapy involves the correction of the overall field matrix, and this might be achieved through suitable balancing or activation of appropriate centres.

The Kirlians, and their supporters throughout the world, have been exploring a *bioplasmic* field for thirty or more years by means of high-frequency electrical photography, using living material as one plate of a high-voltage condenser, and a photographic film between the plates. The corona-discharge generated can produce beautifully coloured pictures with inner and outer aural patterns. To some, these are simply humidity or edge effects, and more a function of the electrical input than the organic tissue. To others, they are a definite representation of the magnetic aura, reflecting states of mind, emotion, and health. The existence of a few photographs – difficult to replicate – showing the original form of a leaf where the physical part had been cut away, and so indicating a biofield independent of matter, has naturally caused considerable controversy.

At the moment, Kirlian methods seem rather hit and miss, with little sense of attempting to establish resonance with basic vibrational modes. And there are medical complications in that the electrical fields tend to trigger off colds and other ailments to which the subject is prone, and cannot be used safely on certain parts of the body because of possible radiation damage – although at the turn of the century, Nikola Tesla obtained remarkable whole-body pictures of himself ignoring such dangers.

In this and some other forms of bioenergetic research, there would seem to be a general assumption that the biofield energies are just outside the normal visual range, thus accounting for the fact that most people cannot see them. Whether in the ultra-violet or the infra-red regions, this should be relatively easy to test with hypnotised people. The lack of evidence in this direction would suggest that the bioenergies are not fundamentally related to these high-frequency ranges. And in fact the quite definite evidence, to be discussed later, that low-frequency magnetic fields can be perceived as patterns of colour, or that trance subjects can describe static magnetic fields, indicates that much of the earlier research into bioenergetics may have been based on an erroneous premise.

The biofield ideas in this book are based on *low-frequency energies, with the spine as the fundamental electrical, gravitational, and developmental axis of the body*. These fields are naturally categorised into two perpendicular force-components. The vertical or longitudinal component relates primarily to internal energy flow, while the transverse fields govern the external structures of skin, muscle, and associated nerves. In the spine itself, and the transverse rib structure, we see the most obvious effects of these two sets of forces. More abstrusely, the vertical meridian contours of the acupoints, and the transverse arrangements of dermatomes, also suggest this.

Some would consider the vertical fields as *biogravitational* in that they assist man to achieve his upright posture, and his balance in complex movements against the action of the earth's gravitational field. The transverse effects can be more definitively called the *biomagnetic* component. This field exists as a natural consequence of the low-frequency currents of the spine, these currents being enveloped by magnetic lines of force according to the basic laws of electromagnetism. It is now just measurable by the new superconducting magnetometers, being something between about one millionth to one billionth of the earth's field near the surface of the body.

For much of the remainder of this book, we will be considering various pieces of indirect evidence relating to the nature of this low-frequency biofield. As yet, there is not too much direct evidence because comparatively little research effort has been directed towards this concept. But major changes are underway, and the first books have recently appeared dealing with low-frequency electromagnetic effects on living organisms. In particular, the concept of a morphogenetic field controlling the development of the embryo is being widely discussed.

Without any biofield concept, all of embryology is a great mystery. And one of the greatest mysteries is the clear-cut differentiation along the spinal axis into transverse sections. With particular interest in transverse effects, this is clearly something of very fundamental importance to us.

After the first few divisions of the fertilised ovum, the cells migrate to an outer periphery; and then at a later stage, one section of this, called the neural plate, folds back on itself to form the neural tube (figure 5.5b). The transverse sectioning occurs along and adjacent to this tube, and from it, the spinal cord and the whole cerebrospinal organisation develop. The *somite* divisions (figure 5.5c) are the most obvious feature of this sectioning process, and relate directly to subsequent spinal and muscle structures. The number of somites indicates the stage of development at any point, and in the human embryo, up to about 44 of these divisions can be observed. It should be noted that three of these, the optic somites, are always quite distinct from the remainder, appearing in the cerebral area.

Existing prior to these developments is the *notochord* (figure 5.5a)

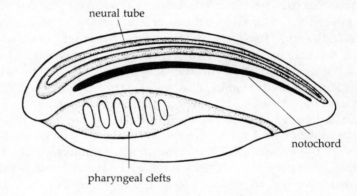

neural tube

notochord

pharyngeal clefts

Fig. 5.5a   General chordate structure

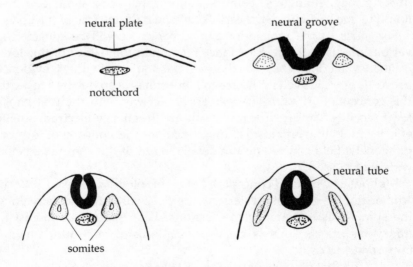

neural plate

neural groove

notochord

somites

neural tube

Fig. 5.5b   Formation of neural tube

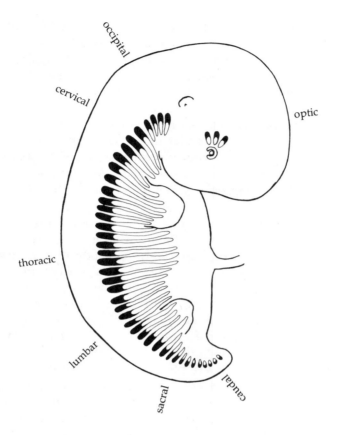

Fig. 5.5c Somites and transverse structuring

which is basic to all vertebrates and the larger class of *chordates*. The neural tube develops close to this and, in the higher vertebrates, the notochord becomes integrated into the spinal material. After the formation of the notochord, neural tube, and somites, many overall aspects of subsequent form are relatively easy to follow. But modern developments in genetics and biochemistry have not thrown any new light on the somite sectioning. In this book, we will be considering the possibility that the somite sections are connected with specific oscillatory centres, and a specific frequency pattern. These centres one would be inclined to associate with the notochord, this being the most basic structure of the chordates.

In biofield terms, the cellular activity in the body can begin to make some sense. Just why one cell becomes a neuron, and another a blood cell, or how cells aggregate into specialised tissues and systems, or why there is such a selective use of gene material in different parts of the body, is so little understood in biochemical terms. But with an overall oscillatory environment creating specific energy patterns at every point of the body, we can understand in general terms how cells seemingly behave in intelligent ways, always maintaining a social cohesion, selecting from the environment just what they need, and rejecting what they do not need. The chemical action of genes and proteins clearly comes under higher levels of control, although possessing a certain autonomy that allows the cell to survive for a time in foreign conditions outside the body. Also we know that when transplanted from one part of the body to another, the cells can adapt to new functions, and to a new geometry.

The aim of the biochemist is to build up a theory of structure from molecules to cells to tissues, etc. But even at the molecular level, there are major problems, particularly with the action of enzymes which are necessary to catalyse almost all chemical activity in the body. Also, through familiarity with molecular concepts, we overlook the mysticism surrounding basic chemical ideas. There was a time, for instance, when the little dashes that denote the bonding forces between elements in chemical diagrams were considered either absurd, or dangerously occult (as with Newton's gravitational theory). But like the virtual phenomena of physics, they are now in routine use. Theoretically, these forces relate to outer electron activity, and in wave mechanics, they receive more sophisticated treatment in vibrational terms. Perhaps one day we will rationalise the mysteries of bonding forces and enzyme activity in oscillatory terms, with natural resonances encouraging the cohesion of stable units, and dissonance causing molecular forms to break up.

What we do understand clearly at the moment is that the physical vitality and chemical properties of molecular material relate very much to the energies, rhythms, and geometry of the bonding forces. Two molecules may have precisely the same atomic units, but if the bonding is different, they may have totally different physical and chemical properties. Even the difference between left-handed and right-handed forms can result in opposite characteristics.

However, beyond the atomic construction of molecules to the cohesion of groups of molecules, the analysis of bonding electromagnetics is quite beyond the quantum theorist. And when we move on to large aggregates of material in cells and tissues, chemistry has to resort to rather vague views of genetic action.

A century ago, the notion of a gene was just an idea, with no physical or chemical basis. Around this idea, tentative theories of inheritance evolved, and also of how the genetic factors organised physical development from ovum to embryo to adult. In earlier theories, it was conceived that each gene controlled one specific feature like the colour of the eyes, but this proved too simple a notion. Gradually, the idea took hold that they worked together, and that one faulty gene could be nullified by the corrective action of others. The concept of 'gene strategy' developed, counteracting the view of discrete action by the individual gene. One did not then have to assume that every single development of the embryo was pre-ordained, but that genes exercised a general guidance over chemical operations, and in particular, affected the rates of reaction.

With the discovery of the helical structure and atomic constitution of DNA, and the associated chemistry leading to protein production, genetic theory is now a specific molecular study, and holding the centre of the stage in biochemical research. The genes are considered to be sections of the DNA within the chromosomal material in the nucleus of the cell. Through the ordering of the four basic molecular building blocks – adenine, thymine, cytosine, and guanine – they organise the amino acids into the complex protein molecules in the outer cytoplasm of the cell, creating enzymes, hormones, transmitters, and other functional compounds. In these processes, the RNA molecule, similar in structure and coding to the DNA, plays a vital intermediary role. The genetic code itself is a very simple one: a sequence of three molecular blocks along the DNA or RNA determines one specific amino acid.

Thus, although all the details are not completely worked out, the basic process of DNA to RNA to protein seems well-established. So, on present understanding, genes produce proteins, the controlling chemicals of the body. But just what sort of process produces the higher multi-cellular forms and overall organisation is not yet known to biochemistry. Protein synthesis through the genes takes us a little way into structural matters, but gives no indication how similar cells with similar chemicals organise themselves so differently according to where they exist geometrically within the body. To theorise on these difficulties, one has to invoke concepts of 'suppressor' genes, genes to control other genes, and many other functional categories.

So the major problems of embryology remain unsolved. Most of the research in genetic chemistry is based on the fruit-fly which has comparatively few genes and breeds very quickly. Thus, it is expected that by selectively tampering with the gene material, one can assess the overall effects on development. In theory, this seems a straightforward thing to do; but as the specialists are well aware, little progress has been made in understanding the development of even this simple organism.

Few today are in a position to query the assumptions of bio-chemists and geneticists. But earlier this century, the highly cultured D'Arcy Thompson, a lone Cambridge scholar indifferent to fashion-able twentieth century opinion, wrote a long treatise on growth and form almost without reference to chemistry and inherited characteris-tics. Although he took an extreme position, there is much for biofield theorists to agree with in his elegant writing.

Matter as such produces nothing, changes nothing, does nothing; and how-ever convenient it may afterwards be to abbreviate our nomenclature and our descriptions, we must most carefully realise at the outset that the sperm-atozoon, the nucleus, the chromosomes or the germ-plasma can never *act* as matter alone, but only as seats of energy and centres of force.

So, dispensing with biochemistry, he goes on to discuss the development of living organisms in terms of mechanics and geometry and number – as, for example, the surface tensions of cellular groups, the struts and ties of bones and ligaments, the geometrical trans-formations relating similar species, the spiral and petal formations derived from periodic functions. However, this physical emphasis is put into suitable perspective.

Of how it is that the soul informs the body, physical science teaches me nothing; and that living matter influences and is influenced by mind is a mystery without a clue. Consciousness is not explained to my comprehen-sion by all the nerve-paths and neurones of the physiologist; nor do I ask of physics how goodness shines in one man's face, and evil betrays itself in another. But of the construction and growth and working of the body, as of all else that is of the earth earthy, physical science is, in my humble opinion, our only teacher and guide.

His thinking still represents a definite challenge to orthodox biochemical and evolutionary theory. The most significant point he made is that cellular forms are inevitably conditioned by the whole force environment, regardless of internal chemistry. Furthermore, until chemical action can be rationalised in more physical terms, chemical theory cannot lead us through to an understanding of physical force and form.

The development of an oscillatory view of organic structure can proceed quite independently of gene theory as now constituted, and should not be regarded as contrary to biochemical ideas. The biofield approach implies the existence of an organised energy matrix which guides the communal activities of the cell, and also influences the genetic chemistry within it. Without such an outside influence, or some means by which one cell can communicate with another, it is difficult to account for the specialised activities and roles in different parts of the body. From the point of view of orthodox physics, this field, including the special centres, must represent the sum of all material effects; but as such, it would be unlikely to have the requisite organising characteristics. Esoterically, and according to the experiments of Harold Burr, the biofield is there from the very beginning, and ready to respond to every stage of development. Either way, we can certainly discuss and analyse how oscillatory centres and fields could bring about the patterning of material, and can leave open the matter of precisely how the genetic material responds to the vibrational environment.

An oscillatory model of organic structure is not completely unfamiliar to physiologists and embryologists working within the orthodox limitations of their subjects. Towards the end of his rather short life, Alan Turing began to ask himself those most basic questions about how a relatively homogeneous spherical shell of material can develop into such a heterogeneous structure as a horse, or whatever. He postulated the existence of two complementary types of chemical organisers, or *morphogens* which, through the normal processes of chemical diffusion, set up standing waveforms whose frequency and amplitude controlled structural development. Mathematically, he was able to show how, from a symmetrical starting point, small instabilities could lead to a very asymmetrical and yet stable development. And using computer simulation methods, he modelled certain dynamic processes that did appear to have some parallels in the simpler organisms of the natural world.

However, to the biologist, it was all rather abstruse, and the mathematics difficult to follow. Nevertheless, his basic idea of structural development through chemical waveforms has remained, and is still considered a distinct possibility for the understanding of growth and form. Work on coupled oscillators and chemical vortices is being developed by a number of researchers; and Ilya Prigogine in particular has made important contributions to the concept of 'self-organisation' through periodic energies.

Such chemical approaches are somewhere between genetic and bioplasmic field concepts, and may help to link them. But much more to the point is the direct structuring of inert material through specific low-frequency waveforms. In the eighteenth century, Chladni demonstrated the patterning of material through oscillatory forces using sand sprinkled on a vibrating plate; and by changing the frequency parameter, the patterns developed in interesting ways. In other words, form was a function of frequency.

Curiously, this experimental work was never really followed up until comparatively recently, although a good deal of effort went into the mathematics. It was left to Hans Jenny, both an artist and scien-

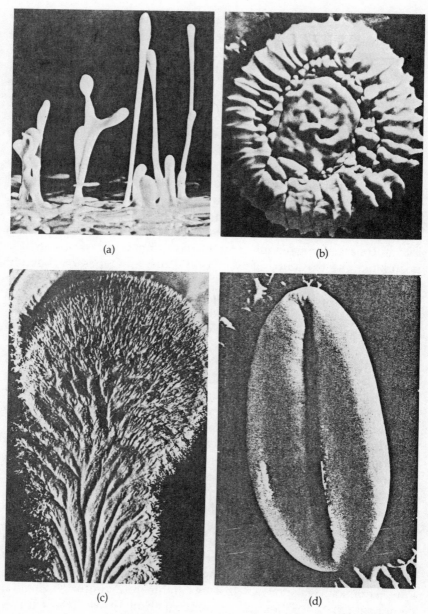

(a)

(b)

(c)

(d)

5.6   Low-frequency cymatic forms (Jenny)

tist, working at the Steiner centre at Dornach in Switzerland, to conduct detailed investigations into the structuring effects of various types of vibrational sources acting on suitably constrained materials. In his science of *cymatics* dealing exclusively with wave and periodic phenomena, he showed that just a single audio frequency of sonic or magnetic energy can produce wonderfully complex forms; and in many cases, his pictures show forms of growth and cell-like structures reminiscent of organic processes (5.6). He continually points out that, in observing natural phenomena, it is so easy to be deceived by the apparent randomness of activity, and to miss the controlling vibrational mechanisms – which may in fact be extremely simple. And commenting on Jenny's work, Lawrence Blair aptly remarks that, without such perception, "the universe is an existential fluke of chemistry with no rhyme or purpose."

It should be noted in these experiments of Chladni and Jenny that the material congregates at the static points of the vibration, leaving the spaces between the particles as the major areas of energy activity. In other words, the vital element is not in the physical appearance of things, but in its essential complement which suitably guides the inert units into the 'dead' areas. Again using Blair's words, "the visible expression of·energy is the inverse of the actual vibrationary pattern, which is invisible". This is the basic problem about discussing living processes in biochemical terms, in that the vibrational environment of material forms is only very dimly perceived, if at all. And yet we know from a multitude of physiological studies that life is, above all, a matter of vibration and frequency.

With computer graphics, we can explore these matters in greater depth, combining as many oscillators as required, and retaining the immediacy of the physical picture. Of particular interest in this book will be *chromatic* frequencies derived from the division of the octave into twelve equal intervals. One finds that certain combinations of these frequencies produce a coherent patterning and polarisation of energy, while other combinations give almost a random appearance. In figure 5.7a, for instance, there are three oscillators in semitone progression, two in one direction and one in the opposite direction. As can be seen, the total effect generates two energy nodes, and field lines linking the two as with the north and south poles of a bar magnet. The more complex pattern of figure 5.7b involves four chromatic oscillators, two in one direction and two in the opposite direction. But just by reversing one of the rotations, the coherence is completely lost.

However, frequency is not the only patterning factor. The amplitude, or radius of rotation, also has a fundamental bearing. The patterns shown in figure 5.8, for instance, were obtained by changing the amplitude of one vector so that the clockwise and anti-clockwise energies balance each other. This tends to produce more symmetrical effects, although in all cases, there is a strong bilateral symmetry such

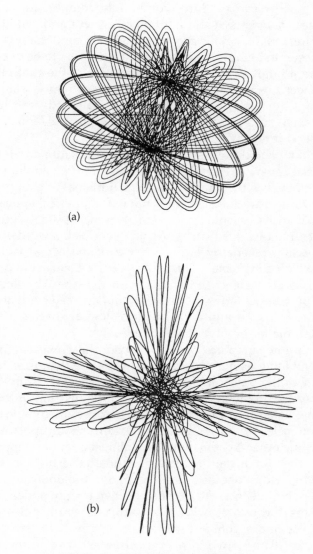

(a)

(b)

Fig. 5.7   'Chromatic' oscillations

as we find in the transverse structuring of vertebrate forms.

The abstract study of three oscillators along these lines is a major undertaking, for the permutations of frequency, amplitude, and direction of rotation are infinite. To those who wish to pursue this matter more deeply, it might be possible to build up a 'patterning

Fig. 5.8 'Balanced' oscillations

language' from certain basic combinations – in fact, an analogue of harmonic theory in music.

The major point to be made in this chapter is that the notion of vibrational centres that control, or help to control the development of the body is a perfectly intelligible one in scientific terms. Behind the cell and its complex molecules and subsystems, there is an oscillatory environment that encourages the cellular units to slot into their natural positions, and also influences the molecular activity within·it. Whether the cell generates the field, or the field generates the cell, or there is a natural action and reaction between them, this is not a crucial issue at this stage. The significant point to be made is that the particle positions, being the visible expression of energy, give just a partial indication of what is going on. Only by trying to conceptualise the complementary biofield patterns as well are we likely to make much causal sense of cellular dynamics.

6. Human Vibrational Patterns

From now on, we will be primarily concerned with the fields and frequencies associated with the cerebrospinal energies of the human organism. Some would argue that the intelligent way to proceed is to concentrate first on the simplest organisms. Unfortunately, with the great paucity of information as regards electrical and electromagnetic activity, this is hardly a practical proposition. Only in the higher vertebrates is there much to go on; and only in man, in EEG studies for example, has much attention been given to frequency aspects. In fact, in order to remove the last traces of vitalism from biology, this type of research has been positively discouraged for much of this century.

From many points of view – the experiments of Hans Jenny, the effects of sound on organic growth, the structural parameters of bones – one is drawn to the conclusion that, whatever the ultimate nature of the biofields, they must involve oscillatory forces in the audio-frequency range. This is part of a natural frequency progression related to varying aggregates of matter. At one end of the spectrum, high-frequency energies like lasers and gamma-rays have very concentrated localised effects on individual atoms and molecules. At the other end, very low frequencies with low energy intensity can move easily through large aggregates of matter, attenuating very little in the process; and at a few cycles per second, we get the basic vibrations connected with the structural forces of the planet. Just one step up from this we have the audio-frequency range that would seem to be the crucial oscillatory level for higher organic development.

This fits in well with neurological understandings of transmission modes and coding mechanisms linking different parts of the nervous system. This activity is quite unlike any modern electrical circuitry, where the current travels at phenomenally high speeds. Along the nerve axons, the diffusion of sodium and potassium ions across the nerve membrane produces an electrical potential; and when a nerve cell discharges, a slow ionic waveform passes down the axon. On reaching a junction, or *synapse*, with another neuron, a chemical transmitter is then released in order to complete the connection. The speed of transmission is of the order of a few metres per second, and the rate of firing nerve discharges is anything from a few pulses per second up to about 700 per second. In other words, the nervous system works in the audio-frequency range, or below.

Concerning the coding of information, it is now a well-established neuroscience principle that information is communicated along the nerve channels through changes in frequency, with energy intensity directly related to the rate of firing of nerve impulses. The amplitude of the pulses remains more or less constant, and therefore cannot convey changing information. Like the binary 1 and 0 structure of modern computers, neuron circuitry functions on a simple on-off basis. So only by changing the speed at which this happens can the 'urgency' of a particular situation be conveyed through the spinal cord to the brain. We also know that on the outward motor circuits from the brain, a basic change in frequency can transform an inhibitory signal into a positive stimulus.

This changing electrical energy of audio-frequency waveforms links in most naturally to the concept of audio-frequency magnetic biofields, with one activating the other according to the laws of electromagnetism. To the materialist, the electrical currents generate the magnetic fields; to the esotericist, the magnetic fields regulate nervous action. Either way, we come to much the same viewpoint of the electromagnetic vibrational environment, although with different ideas of causation.

The magnetic fields associated with the ionic currents can now be measured, even though the environmental fields are several orders of magnitude larger near the skin surface. This work has been undertaken mainly for medical purposes, including comparison with the field potentials recorded by the electro-cardiogram (ECG) and electro-encephalogram (EEG). Taking both the magnetic and electrical data together, rather than just the electrical, more can be inferred about the nature of the source currents creating the electromagnetic field.

The first measurements, about twenty years ago, were taken of the magnetic field near the heart, and were made with two similar coils each containing several million turns of wire. The purpose of the two compensating coils was to filter out all background magnetism, including the earth's magnetic field (0.5 gauss), and artificial fields from mains sources of about 10^{-3} gauss. The next measurements a few years later were taken with the new *superconducting quantum interference device* (SQUID), and using a heavily shielded room to screen out almost all trace of the environmental fields. Since then, working on the same principle as the coil measurements, two SQUID devices have been used, this obviating the need for special screening.

In measurements with the SQUID, fields as low as 10^{-10} gauss can be registered, although this sensitivity decreases with frequency. The maximum field strengths around the heart are of the order of 10^{-6} gauss, and frequencies up to 500 Hz have been recorded. Around the head, the field strengths are about a hundred times smaller, and the low-frequency magnetic waveforms correspond closely with the EEG brain waves below about 30 Hz. Higher frequencies in the cerebral region would be close to the limits of sensitivity.

It should be kept in mind that these measurements are taken a few centimetres from the body. From such a position, the field strengths are exceptionally weak; but close to the cerebrospinal channel, they could be several orders of magnitude greater.

The magnetic field as described by Eileen Garrett would seem to relate most naturally to this low-frequency electromagnetic environment, representing on the one hand a sort of residue of physical energy, and on the other, a higher level of control, above that of the nervous system. In perceptual terms, the common characteristic of these biofields is colour – thus indicating that low-frequency fields can be perceived through the visual systems. This fortunately we can verify for ourselves without any special psychical abilities. If for instance, a strong audio-frequency electromagnetic field is applied to the head in the waking state – or a weak field in a light hypnotic state – then colour patterns will be immediately experienced. And by making changes in frequency corresponding to specific musical notes, different colours will present themselves to the senses. Moreover, this will be perceived when the eyes are closed, thus suggesting a more direct effect on the mind or brain than with the normal visual experience of high-frequency light photons being filtered through the eye. Technologists have been aware of such phenomena – *magnetic phosphenes* – since the beginning of the century.

This line of thought leads directly to the old controversy about possible correlations between sound and colour vibrations. Sir Isaac Newton, that most troubling dissident of all philosophical 'isms', so often criticised for his occult interests, certainly surprised his scientific colleagues by suggesting a simple relationship between the seven colours of the spectrum and the 7-note minor scale. Then later he was furiously attacked for a completely false theory of light by the esotericists – particularly Goethe and his followers – who somehow failed to distinguish between the process of combining physical rays, and the subjective effects of combining pigments. Suggestions of this misunderstanding still exist today within the Steiner movement.

With our modern knowledge, it is difficult to understand what all

the fuss has been about. Through our understanding of the electromagnetic nature of light, together with our knowledge of wave
motion, frequency, harmonics, and resonance, we can relate simply
any octave of frequencies to any other octave, including audio vibrations to the colour spectrum. As has been stated, the complete electromagnetic panorama of aetheric waves, or resonating energy
quanta, however you want to conceptualise it, consists as far as we
know of about 80 octaves, with visible light representing fairly precisely one octave of this from about 385 to 770 billion (10^{12}) cycles per
second. Through the different frequency sensitivities of the three
types of retinal cones of the visual system, the individual vibrations
within the light octave trigger off low-frequency impulses in the cerebral nerves, and are interpreted by the psyche as specific colours.

Obviously we can divide this octave of colour at will into regions
that can correspond directly to any given musical or sonic divisions.
In doing this, it must be understood that, because of the basic differences between the visual and auditory systems, a colour in general
represents a range or combination of frequencies, whereas a musical
note consists of a particular frequency, combined with harmonics in
higher octaves. However, this is essentially a physical matter related
to differences in methods of decoding between the visual and auditory systems; but conceptually, we can certainly make a direct (1–1)
correspondence between audio and light frequencies.

Helping to reinforce this conceptual correlation at a mental level is
the idea that the progression from octave to octave is cyclic in nature.
Beginning, for instance, at middle C, and proceeding up the diatonic
scale, our senses experience a return to C, followed by the continua-
tion of a similar sequence in the next octave, although with a definite
subjective difference that we describe in lower-higher terms – thus
suggesting a spiralling movement from one level to another. In the
visual area, we cannot experience different octave levels because only
one octave of electromagnetic energy is processed by the optic system. But we can infer indirectly the cyclic progression of colour
through the deep red-purple, almost brown, which links the red and
violet ends of the colour spectrum – both for the scientist dealing with
physical rays, and for the artist with his colour circle of pigments.

The mathematical division of the Western musical scale goes back
to Pythagoras and his experiments in the division of a stretched
string. From his basic ideas of natural harmonics and mathematical
ratio, through the subsequent development of modes and scales,
through the curious and sometimes startling effects in the progression from one key to another, we have arrived at the modern chromatic scale of twelve equally-spaced semitones, from which diverse

forms of music have been created with profound and immediate impact on cerebral and bodily activity. There are other divisions of the scale – and some more complex in Indian music – but no other equal division of the octave would seem to have that inner, intrinsic power of generating an emotional mood or climate. Also, in the purely mathematical sense, no other homogeneous division of the octave (unless one goes down to quarter-tones or related fractions) allows for such a close correspondence with the precise intervals arising from natural resonance.

Summarising briefly the basic frequency data behind the modern chromatic scale, the following table gives the first nine natural harmonics of the note C with a frequency which, for convenience, we will define as 1.

note	harmonics									
C	C	G	C	E	G	B♭	C	D	E	...
frequency 1	2	3	4	5	6	7	8	9	10	...

This gives us the following pure major intervals or resonances.

interval	2nd	3rd	4th	5th	6th
frequency ratio	9/8	5/4	4/3	3/2	5/3

The 7th can be derived from a 5th + 3rd, giving the ratio 15/8 ($3/2 \times 5/4$). From these intervals, the pure-tone major scale can be constructed as follows.

	C	D	E	F	G	A	B	C
frequency	1	9/8	5/4	4/3	3/2	5/3	15/8	2
interval		9/8	10/9	16/15	9/8	10/9	9/8	16/15

As can be seen from the second line which gives interval, or ratio of frequencies, such a scale with perfect resonances involves three distinct types of basic interval – tones 9/8, 10/9, and semitone 16/15. Beginning from different notes on this scale, we obtain the old *modes* of ecclesiastical music. Unfortunately these do not allow for natural modulation to other keys, and restrict the development of fixed-note

note	pure scale	modern scale	% error
C	1	1	
D	1.125	1.122	−0.2
E	1.25	1.260	+0.8
F	1.333 ..	1.335	+0.1
G	1.5	1.498	−0.1
A	1.666 ..	1.682	+0.9
B	1.875	1.888	+0.7

instruments. The basic problem of the pure-tone scale is its three intervals. However by redefining the semitone to allow twelve equally-spaced notes, the original notes and intervals are preserved to a high degree of accuracy, and obvious restrictions removed. For 12 equal intervals, the semitone ratio must be the 12th root of 2, or 1.0594631 . . .

Constructing a chromatic scale that resonates with a similar scale in the light octave is quite simply done in numerical terms. Beginning, for instance, from the note A above middle C at the international pitch of 440 cycles per second (Hertz), we need to multiply this by 2^{40} to give a frequency in the visual spectrum 40 octaves above. This gives an orange vibration of approximately 484×10^{12} Hz. However, this does not produce a very suitable colour correspondence, the colour notes not being centrally placed within the colour bands. In particular, the note F would correspond with a frequency at the extreme red end. But with a little trial and error, one can arrive at a table involving correspondences close to the mean positions for specific colours. The following chromatic scale is based on the scientific middle C of 256 Hz, this being a little below standard pitch.

TABLE 6.1

	note	audio (Hz)	light (10^{12} Hz)	colour
	F	683	751	purple (P)
	E	645	709	violet (V)
	E♭	609	669	indigo (I)
Yang	D	575	632	blue (B)
	D♭	542	596	blue-green (BG)
	C	512	563	green (G)
	B	483	531	yellow-green (YG)
	B♭	456	502	yellow (Y)
	A	431	473	orange (O)
Yin	A♭	406	447	orange-red (OR)
	G	384	422	red (R)
	G♭	362	398	ruby-red (RR)

This gives us a nice symmetry between the warm positive side of the spectrum, and the cool negative side. The colours and notes form a closed perceptual circle, with yellow-green as the transitional colour from Yin to Yang, and purple as the transition from Yang to Yin. Note that these colour polarities are contrary to the Chinese convention of showing Yin as blue and Yang as red. But in the sense that physical vitality is Yin, and Yang is the controller of Yin, the opposite convention seems the more natural to the Western mind.

This is essentially Isaac Newton's correspondence expanded to the 12-note scale, although he had no knowledge of electromagnetic waves. Today there is a little more practical basis for such a correspondence, which is not without relevance to biofield studies. Evidence comes from various musical-visual experiments, investigations into the physical and mental effects of sound, and attempts to assess how different colours affect the body. Not that any of this would come into the realms of 'hard' science, and so we will content ourselves with just a few comments on the major points of interest in this work.

On the perceptual aspects, it has been discovered that, apart from the coloured field patterns around the head caused by audio-frequency magnetism as mentioned earlier, there are a few people who clearly experience colour with a musical note, and colour patterns with a musical composition. The reverse seems much less common, although composers such as Debussy, Delius, and Messiaen presumably had such perceptual ability, translating the natural visual world into musical patterns. These psychological studies come under the general heading of *synaesthesia*, and the evidence includes the visual effects of different instruments and styles of composition, and the colour qualities of major and minor keys. In a few studies, direct correspondences have been suggested between musical notes and colours, some of it roughly consistent with our mathematical correlation. Other evidence would need to be interpreted on the basis that mental colour is the complement to physical colour in order to be consistent. Overall, these studies indicate a specific sound-colour correlation with a limited number of people. Physiologically, this would imply some overlap within the brain between the low-frequency audio and visual systems.

Concerning the effects of particular colours on the body, little has been done in this area for the past forty years, it being superseded by more dangerous experimentation with frequencies both below and above the visual region. Today, the old chromotherapists are regarded with some disdain – probably because they were sometimes involved with clairvoyant assistants who endeavoured to assess directly just what effects different colours were having. Certainly it is very difficult to analyse the effects of 'visual notes' in the short-term: colour, unlike sound, makes its impact on the body in the longer-term through the chemical action of hormones. However, using a minimum of technology, these researchers came to many interesting conclusions about the properties of each colour, and the treatment of specific conditions through definite patterns of colour. Of fundamental importance in their thinking was the fairly natural idea that the positive Yin colours stimulated, and the negative Yang colours exerted a balancing and regulatory influence over physical function. The extremes of red and violet had to be used with great caution, with orange, yellow, green, and blue the most useful in treatment. The central point of the spectrum, about yellow-green, was considered as basically neutral in effect.

More conventionally acceptable research has been done in the area of the specific effects of colours on the endocrines. These results indicate, for instance, that the testes respond most to green, the parathyroid to blue, and the adrenal cortex and thyroid to violet. With other glands, the results are less conclusive. It would probably be unwise to take these results too definitively, but they can be kept at the back of the mind.

Research into the effects of sonic energy on the body is of course a much more straightforward matter. On the destructive side, we know that very low infrasonic frequencies of a few cycles per second can be physically harmful, even to the extent of causing death through the collapse of the internal organs. Very high frequencies can be both physically and mentally disturbing; and above the audio range, ultrasonic energy tends to decalcify and soften bones. In fact, it can be argued that all sonic energy is potentially destructive, as illustrated by famous singers who shatter glasses through resonance, or by the mantric stimulation of kundalini energy which, unless carefully controlled, can be explosive in its effects. The modern pop music scene is unfortunately only too well aware of these effects, and sometimes deliberately aims to produce both physical and mental disturbance. But on the constructive side, the carefully prepared and calculated effects of serious and popular musical composition are conducive to our general well-being in the fullest sense.

Music is an emotional language that affects the psychic centres from the midbrain regions right down the spine to the sexual centre. The spinal cord, or chord, is the sounding board, and the vertebral centres resonate appropriately to melody, harmony, and modulation. From the first cervical to the last lumbar segment of the spine, one observes the most precisely engineered structure of the body – both in the embryological state and the adult human (figure 6.1). There is an exactness, a homogeneity in size, spacing, and positioning of the vertebrae similar to a stretched string where the spacing for equal intervals of sound varies according to geometric progression. Taking into account that the spinal nerve transmissions resonate in the audio

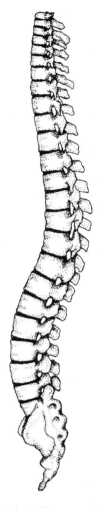

Fig. 6.1   Human spine

range of frequencies, one suspects some definite musical pattern along this central meridian, with each vertebral section or associated nerve representing a definite note on this physiological keyboard of controls.

These ideas about sound, colour, and human structure, surely provide some clues about the low-frequency organisation of the human biofields. Studying these fields through direct technological measurement is exceptionally difficult, and as we have seen, only recently have there been sufficiently sensitive magnetometers for recording the external fields. Doubtless, in time, we will attempt to measure these forces within the body, as well as outside. But however sophisticated our experimental techniques become, there is always the danger that, in the absence of any theoretical conceptualisation of these fields, we may be swamped with masses of data that we are unable to interpret in any meaningful way.

All research requires a blend of intuitive theorising and controlled experiment. Taking into account ideas about relative frequency, distribution of nerves and dermatomes, acupuncture relationships, the tentative results of chromotherapy, the effects of music and sound-colour correspondence, and many other matters that have been discussed, we should be able to make some intelligent guess about a possible set of audio-frequencies related to spinal positions. This can then be suitably modified in the light of practical experience and experiment.

As with chromosome structure, one would expect some general pattern, some overall frequency organisation for the human organism, although with small differences between individuals and between male and female. The table 6.2, based principally on theoretical considerations, although taking into account the limited experimental evidence available, indicates one possible way of expressing such a frequency organisation.

This highly speculative table attempts to incorporate some of the ideas so far discussed, and the range of frequencies in the trunk is compatible with our knowledge of transmission rates within the nervous system. The range of something over two octaves in the spine agrees with our vibrational interpretation of Yoga ideas; and the frequency of about 500 hz in the lower cervical position is consistent with the measured rate of electrical vibration in the nerve pathways of the arm for simple pressure on the fingers. Whether or not the colour associations have objective significance, they can at least be thought of as a visual method of categorising frequency.

In autonomic terms, it should be noted that the sacral nerves are parasympathetic or Yang, and the upper thoracic and lumbar sections are essentially sympathetic or Yin. The endocrinal positions are roughly consistent with the chakral resonances, and also with the purported colour sensitivities of each gland. The association points of acupuncture linking spinal positions to internal organs and meridians consist of the twelve separate tones of the chromatic sequence.

As for the cranial nerves of the brainstem, one wonders whether these constitute another vibrational octave, each nerve having a distinctive function. Also, from the form of the whole body, and the obvious discontinuity in form from trunk to head, one suspects a definite break in the ascending sequence of frequency.

TABLE 6.2

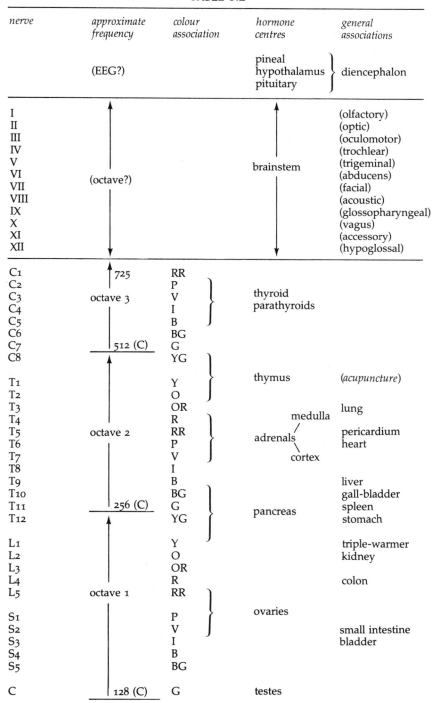

nerve	approximate frequency	colour association	hormone centres	general associations
	(EEG?)		pineal hypothalamus pituitary } diencephalon	
I				(olfactory)
II				(optic)
III				(oculomotor)
IV				(trochlear)
V			brainstem	(trigeminal)
VI	(octave?)			(abducens)
VII				(facial)
VIII				(acoustic)
IX				(glossopharyngeal)
X				(vagus)
XI				(accessory)
XII				(hypoglossal)
C1	725	RR		
C2		P		
C3	octave 3	V	thyroid parathyroids	
C4		I		
C5		B		
C6		BG		
C7	512 (C)	G		
C8		YG		
T1		Y	thymus	(acupuncture)
T2		O		
T3		OR		lung
T4		R	medulla	
T5	octave 2	RR	adrenals	pericardium
T6		P		heart
T7		V	cortex	
T8		I		
T9		B		liver
T10		BG		gall-bladder
T11	256 (C)	G	pancreas	spleen
T12		YG		stomach
L1		Y		triple-warmer
L2		O		kidney
L3		OR		
L4		R		colon
L5	octave 1	RR		
S1		P	ovaries	
S2		V		small intestine
S3		I		bladder
S4		B		
S5		BG		
C	128 (C)	G	testes	

The three upper centres of the central thalamic core of the brain relate to the highest hormonal and psychical controls – the frontal centres to autonomic control, and the more posterior pineal to conscious control. One would expect these frequencies to be related to the alpha and beta waves of the EEG, and in the next chapter, we will attempt to expand on this aspect.

In its overall form, this differential frequency structure relates closely to the organisation of the somite sections in the embryo, with over forty centres connected with the cerebrospinal divisions of the nervous system, and three separated ones in the cranial region. These three optic somites in the head are a common feature of almost all vertebrates, being intimately related to the development of the visual system and eye muscles.

The associations with various physical organs should not be taken too specifically, for the table is attempting to understand the basic organisation of something behind the physical systems as we now understand them. It may have a fairly direct association with the primitive forms of the notochord and the somites in the embryo; but in the developed structures of the body, there can be no simple one-one correspondence. The tissues and activities of any particular organ represent the complex sum of the effects of all the force-centres, although one centre, and perhaps one nerve, may have a particular influence over it.

Nor should the frequencies be taken too definitively. While they may indicate some overall mean, there are obviously differences in frequency patterns for every single person. Between the healthy person and the sufferer of chronic conditions, there are probably quite large differences, but not so large as would be incompatible with the basic physical structuring and functioning. The phrases we use in everyday language such as being off-key, off-colour, in tune, keyed up, probably represent something close to the truth. Perhaps each centre has a restricted range of vibrations, and through mental and emotional energy, or through externally-applied energies, it is possible to speed things up or slow things down a little, as with the brainwaves. In all types of medical therapy, stimulation and sedation, constriction and dilation, overactive and underactive states, are clearly recognised, and naturally relate to these frequency concepts.

The structural aspects, as distinct from the functional aspects of these ideas are best considered in relation to the embryo rather than fully developed organisms. The earliest development of the embryo, right from the fusion of two single cells, is obviously fundamental to all future development. At later stages, the material inevitably acquires a degree of inertia, and physical structure can subsequently be modified only to a very limited degree. But at the early stages, in the formation of the spherical ring of cells called the *blastula*, followed by an inward movement to create the inner, middle, and outer layers of the *gastrula* (endoderm, mesoderm, ectoderm), the embryologist can to some extent cause the growth to proceed along different and distorted lines. What one might eventually hope to achieve in this vibrational theorising is to account for the cell migrations in the blastula and gastrula, together with the folding of the neural tube and the appearance of the somite sections along the tube (Fig. 5.5b). At this point, the stage is then set for the development of the nervous system, the muscles, and the whole cerebrospinal structure.

In the chordates, of which the vertebrates are a subset, we have seen there is a common structural plan, with a linear development from head to tail related to the notochord. Somite differentiation takes place along this chord which, in the higher vertebrates, fuses into the spinal column. Thus, it might be possible to model the general chordate plan in terms of a set of oscillators along the notochord and, by consideration of the wave potentials, follow the pattern of structuring forces that govern early embryonic development. In the non-chordates, one must assume that the oscillators are not arranged in this linear geometrical way. Presumably, the way in which they do arrange themselves is determined by relative frequency – certain patterns being stable in some linear or helical arrangement, while others naturally gravitate towards a more centralised or closed geometrical system.

A little thought will show that a simple linear arrangement of force-centres is unlikely to account for the asymmetries between the right and left sides of the body. For instance, near the spine there are small asymmetries like the kidneys, with one just a little higher than the other. Towards the front of the body, there are major asymmetries in organs like the liver, pancreas, and intestines. To account for these factors, and yet retaining some overall degree of symmetry in right and left-handed development, one might envisage paired or coupled oscillators arranged as in figure 6.2a.

There is in fact a reasonably convincing case to be made for such an arrangement. As discussed in chapter 5, two similar rotations with small difference frequency create a vortex. Thus the adjacent oscillators on each side would form pairs of vortices with opposite rotations – such pairing being a common feature of vortex motion. This then implies transverse patterning processes of the form shown in figure 6.2b. Vortical effects of this nature would be consistent with the

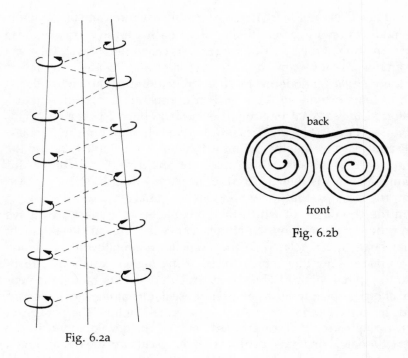

Fig. 6.2b

Fig. 6.2a

overall bilateral symmetry, with the small asymmetries near the spine, and with the general asymmetry between the back and front of the body.

Assuming 46 centres as in Table 6.2, this would indicate an oscillatory structure arranged into 23 pairs. Curiously, this is the way the chromosomes are organised, with 23 derived from the male, and 23 from the female. But this is perhaps not so surprising in that the breaking up of nuclear material as the cell is about to divide into chromosome units is the most basic form of segmentation we know. However, if the numbers are more than coincidence, we would expect to find similar relationships in other vertebrates. But just taking the structural parameters of the chicken, with a chromosome number of 78, 52 somite sections, 39 + 12 main nerves, and 42–47 vertebral sections, it is difficult to know what to make of this. Nevertheless, the orderly arrangement and progression of form always to be found in the chromosome structures (figure 6.3) is rather striking.

This proposed arrangement of oscillators suggests the three fundamental channels of control down the spine. There is the inner channel associated with conscious control, and the two outer channels automatically regulating the internal organs and processes of the

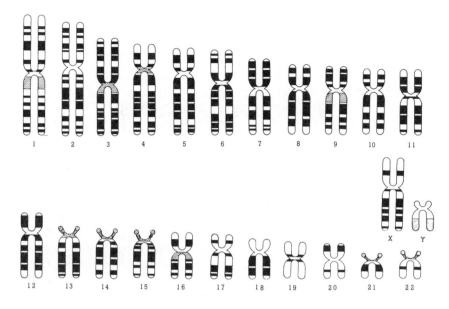

Fig. 6.3   Human chromosomes (male XY, female XX)

body. In Western and Chinese terms, the outer channels as defined by the autonomic chains of neurons and by the bladder meridians, form a simple linear arrangement. However, Yoga theory indicates a double helix coiling round the spine, with complementary male and female chains of energy (Ida and Pingala) through which the kundalini energy gives vitality to the body. Normally the central channel has only indirect effects on the outer channels. But it would seem that, through the control of breath, and through visualisation, conscious and unconscious forces can be yoked together, energising and recharging the whole organism.

In this general discussion of the vertebrate biofields, we have perhaps the beginnings of a conceptual model containing ideas of frequency and positioning. Just from a therapeutic point of view, this may have some usefulness. But to pursue this further in theoretical terms, we require more specific ideas, which involve electromagnetics, waveforms, and computational techniques. This we will do in chapter 8. In the meantime, we will make a deviation, a purposeful one, into some aspects of brain structure and function, including a discussion of EEG research. Obviously any theoretical model of the biofields must take into account the brainwaves, the one aspect of human functioning that has been intensively investigated in frequency terms.

7. Cerebral Centres

In Western thought, the so-called mind-brain problem continues to hold a central place. On one side of the debate, the problem is essentially one of language, in that the subjective qualities of mind are simply convenient descriptions of physiological processes in the brain. It is like the discussion of higher-level languages in computers where it is too clumsy to talk about individual machine instructions, and one gives functional names to more complex groups of instructions. With this viewpoint, it is envisaged that what is now described in psychological, or literary, or commonsense terms, can ultimately be reduced to physical processes. To many people, such *reductionism* is a disturbing thought, apparently reducing us to a machine status. The alternative to this is to postulate some non-material entity, a ghost in the machine, that somehow activates the physical controls. So, in these rather primitive either-or terms, either matter is mind, or there is an immediate transition from mind to matter. The idea of a hierarchy of levels, a pluralisation from mind to matter, is quite unnecessarily complex for those who theorise exclusively by the law of parsimony. A most obvious *intermediate* issue concerning the forces responsible for structuring the brain, as distinct from operating it, generally gets no consideration.

In the experimental fields of psychology and physiology, the interest now centres on what correlations can be made between mental and neuronal functioning; and this is discussed in terms of localisation of effects in the cerebral cortex. First efforts at localisation theory were made by the phrenologists of the last century who ascribed to various regions of the skull different mental and emotional characteristics. Although this was laughed out of court by the scientists, it was not long before the neuroscientists had produced a sort of phrenology of their own, and their version has now become the basis for psychical-physical models of cerebral functioning (figures 7.1a, 7.1b).

Most of our knowledge of brain function, and localisation of effects in different areas of the cortex, has come from brain surgeons operating on epileptics without general anaesthesia. In this way, patient and surgeon can explore the brain together in the conscious state. In

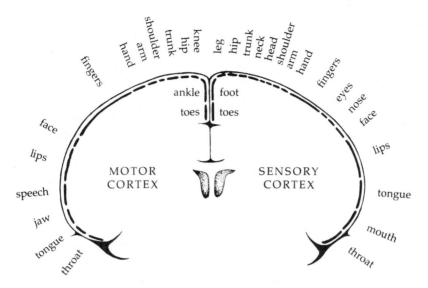

Fig. 7.1b   Motor/sensory cortex

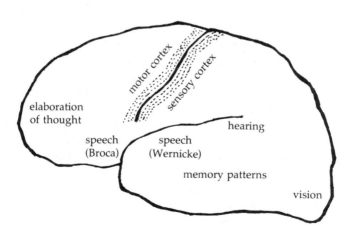

Fig. 7.1a   Neuro-phrenology

recent years, Wilder Penfield has caused a good deal of controversy in scientific circles by coming to the conclusion after a lifetime of operating on the brain that the results of his work are most naturally interpreted in terms of a separation of mind and brain. In this, his position is the same as his mentor, the great pioneer of brain research, Sir Charles Sherrington.

Such viewpoints have not been fashionable in medical circles for a very long time. Most other researchers take as axiomatic that mind is simply an aspect of brain functioning. But Penfield came to the simple dualist conclusion, mainly because the patient was always aware that he himself played no part in whatever muscle or mental stimulation occurred – the conscious self was always a passive observer to what was going on.

In the epileptic operations, parts of the brain are exposed by removing sections of skull, and different points are probed with a small oscillatory current – in the case of Penfield, this was a square waveform of 60 cycles per second. In doing this, he made the assumption that one was either interfering with normal electrical processes, or activating neurons in other parts of the body. The particular waveform he used, or any magnetic effect, or hormonal stimulation, does not seem to have been considered relevant. For getting a general feel about cortical function, this was fair enough. But as already implied in our discussion of frequency, the choice of waveform may have had a definite bearing and bias on the central brain structures.

Two of the most obvious effects obtainable by these vibrational methods are the stimulation or inhibition of muscle activity, and the bringing to consciousness of the long-term experiential memory, with pictures, sounds, sensations, and feelings similar to those experienced in hypnotic regression.

Muscles can be activated from the *motor cortex*, and from many other positions. The left cortex controls the muscles on the right of the body, and vice versa. Memory is activated from the *temporal cortex*, and also by probing more deeply through to the *hippocampus* near the top of the brainstem. Removal of cortical material does not erase memories as far as can be judged; but removal of the complete hippocampus, although leaving the long-term memory intact, makes it very difficult to establish new memory patterns that are accessible to the conscious mind.

Apart from muscle and memory effects, there has been much research effort into the speech mechanisms which exist on just one side of the brain – left or dominant side for the right-handed person, and about evenly divided between right and left sides for left-handed people. Speech is an especially complex phenomenon involving many muscles connected with the throat, as well as being completely bound up with memory and language structure. Vibrational probing, and evidence from brain damage, suggest two main speech areas, and two main categories of *aphasia* or language difficulty. There is Broca's region in the frontal cortex, where damage or interference produces ungrammatical, yet meaningful speech, and difficulty in finding or enunciating appropriate words. And there is Wernicke's region at the intersection of temporal, parietal, and occipital lobes where malfunction produces apparently fluent speech which makes, however, no obvious sense.

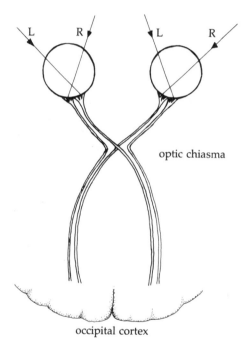

Fig. 7.2   Optic pathways

The one functional region of the cortex most clearly established is the visual area at the back of the brain. There are two completely definable optic tracts, merging and crossing at the optic chiasma in the hypothalamus region, and then proceeding towards the occipital area (figure 7.2). It can be seen that signals from the right visual field, for both eyes, go essentially to the left hemisphere, and the left visual field to the right. While it cannot be said that any particular piece of cortex contains a specific part of an image, damage to these regions produces fairly predictable defects of sight. When the occipi-

tal area is activated by vibrational probes, the effect is more related to
our internal world, producing the sort of colour patterns one gets
when the eyes are closed. Also, as noted before, from certain points
of stimulation, rotational discs of colour are observed – thus either
giving the chakral forms some objective basis, or suggesting an aber-
ration of visual functioning, or both. However, whatever the doubts
about the phrenology of other parts of the cortex, all evidence from
the occipital region is unequivocal about its functional relationship
to visual perception.

Penfield was surprised to discover that the removal of quite large
sections of the cortex produced little change, and no loss of consciousness. This led him to conclude that consciousness and the
highest integrative and interpretative functions were most clearly
associated with the central core of the brain at the top of the brainstem – referring to it as the *centrencephalic* region. The main part of
this is the diencephalon, containing the *thalamus* in the central section, the *hypothalamus* that controls the pituitary in the anterior section, and the *epithalamus* that incorporates the pineal in the posterior
section. Through this region, all the sensations coming from the
spinal and cranial nerves are filtered, and appropriate motor actions
through the nerves to the muscles are organised and coordinated.
Also, from the information obtained from epileptic patients, the centrencephalic core would seem to be the focus of mental activity and
the gateway to long-term memory (figures 7.3a, 7.3b).

Much has been written in recent years of the various polarities of
the hemispheres, with the major cortex related to rationality, time,
language, analysis, and sequential processes generally, while the
minor cortex is associated with spatial, intuitive, and synthesising
functions. Alternatively, although not clearly consistent with these
characteristics, or with the fact that the left hemisphere is dominant for
most people of either sex, the major cortex is often categorised as
male and Yang, and the minor cortex as female or Yin. However, in
the tendency of women to trust their intuition, and of men to rely on
the slower analytical processes, this makes general sense. Electromagnetic evidence indicates opposite magnetic polarisation between the two hemispheres.

There have been some unusual experiments carried out with
epileptic patients who have had the nerve fibres of the Corpus Cal-
losum cut, so severing neuronal communication between the two
sides. In this situation, the two hemispheres appear to assume quite
separate roles, even personalities, with the normal conscious processes of mind and memory clearly related to the dominant side, and
the minor side functioning in automatic mode. Where the hemi-

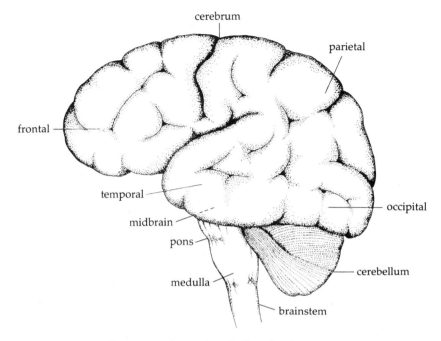

Fig. 7.3a   Cortex/cerebellum/brainstem

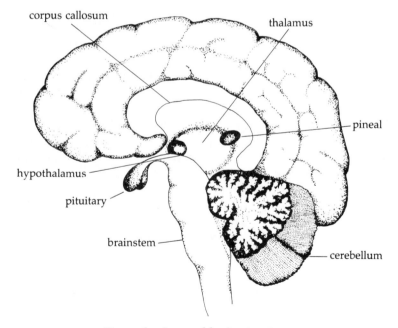

Fig. 7.3b   Internal brain structure

spheres are completely detached from each other in this way, the visual fields of the two eyes do provide some coordinating link. But by carefully screening the light entering each eye, it has been demonstrated that, *quite unknown to the conscious subject*, the minor hemisphere can independently interpret words, and subsequently communicate appropriate actions to the left hand – including the writing of words in a different script.

This definitely seems to indicate that the cerebral psyche is divided into two complementary forms. It also suggests possible methods of dissociation of conscious and unconscious aspects, such as the modern hypnotic technique of concentrating on the left visual field and the left side of the body. It raises interesting questions of control in automatic writing, and in curious forms of speech under trance. However, fascinating though this field of research is, it is not now such an obvious conclusion to draw that the psychical division is completely synonymous with the cortical division, for there are people who function quite normally with one hemisphere badly damaged or even completely removed.

Apart from serious brain damage, we know that if the speech controls of a child are damaged in the dominant hemisphere, it will probably not be long before alternative speech areas will appear in the other cortex. Much recent theorising about the functional polarities of the hemispheres has not been substantiated, and would seem at the least to be something less than the whole truth. We can look at the cortex from other angles and find other distinctions. The frontal cortex is considered to be related to mental processes, in contrast to more posterior areas of the brain which coordinate movement and control physical balance. There are different and complementary polarities not only from side to side, but from front to back, and to some extent from lower to upper. The existence of definite anterior and posterior endocrine centres (and associated psychical centres of brow and crown) perhaps helps to correct the over-simplicity of the present cortical models of brain function.

A simple 2-dimensional model in horizontal section through the centrencephalic core, as shown below (figure 7.4), is distinctly reminiscent of Jung's psychological interpretation of the ancient Chinese symbolism of Yin and Yang which naturally expresses several geometrical polarities.

The forward centre, together with right and posterior regions, reflects unconscious and autonomic Yin activity; while the complementary Yang centre, in association with left and frontal areas, is related to conscious functions and controls. Certainly these are meaningful patterns consistent with the general evidence.

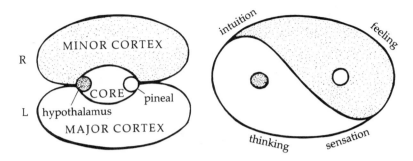

Fig. 7.4

However, from a 3-dimensional viewpoint, it seems necessary to consider at least three basic centres of energy, with the frontal centre containing two separate components. This is suggested by the two eyes, the two hemispheres, and the two sections of the pituitary, among other things. The posterior pituitary is really part of the hypothalamus which, in controlling the emotional tone, can be thought of as the intermediary between the anterior pituitary and the pineal. There is a progression from unconscious to conscious, from lower to upper, from inner to outer, in the functional aspects of the pituitary, hypothalamus, and pineal centres. In terms of brow position, we might well refer to these centres as lowbrow, middlebrow, and highbrow!

Perhaps related to this idea is the strange acupuncture organ called the *triple-warmer* which has always been a mystery to Western physiology. In Chinese texts, it is perceived as a triple envelope of the body giving warmth and protection, and thus seeming to have some connection with the inner, middle, and outer biofields that are considered to reflect vitality, emotion, and mental processes. Both by virtue of its function as a temperature controller, and the meridian position, many Western practitioners of acupuncture now relate the triple-warmer directly to the hypothalamus. However, a more comprehensive idea is that the triple-warmer refers to all three endocrine centres, with three specific waveforms determining the three distinctive aspects of the cerebral fields (figure 7.5).

It is interesting to consider the brainwave activity as measured by the electro-encephalogram (EEG) in terms of three distinct centres, with three basic structuring frequencies. EEG research has concentrated mainly on frequencies below about 30 cycles per second (Hz), and these are subdivided into four categories. In the highest frequency category above 12 Hz are the *beta* waves, which are much in evidence around the frontal areas in the waking state, and particu-

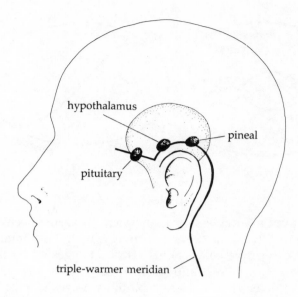

hypothalamus

pineal

pituitary

triple-warmer meridian

Fig. 7.5

larly during concentrated mental activity. A typical beta frequency is about 22 Hz. The next frequency level contains the *alpha* waves of 8–12 Hz which are normally recorded from the back or sides of the head. At the upper end of this range are our most basic waveforms, occurring when the eyes are closed and the mind relaxed. At the lower end, there are waves that seem to indicate special meditative or clinical states. The normal alpha waves disappear when the eyes are open, but this is not necessarily the case with the abnormal alpha waves (figure 7.6).

Below these are the *theta* waves of 4–7 Hz, which cannot be clearly identified with any one psychic state. They may occur in emotional trauma, or in the transition from relaxed to deep sleep states. They may indicate a state of trance, or some degree of mental retardation – being quite natural in younger children. Finally, in the lowest frequency category are the *delta* waves of 1–3 Hz which occur in deep sleep.

Roughly, the overall frequency pattern reflects a natural progression from the alert waking state down to the deepest levels of sleep; and within this waveband are the special frequencies of about 7–9 Hz that indicate something distinct from normal waking consciousness and sleep. The categories given apply essentially to adult experience –

by and large, frequencies are lower in young children. Some representative patterns are given below.

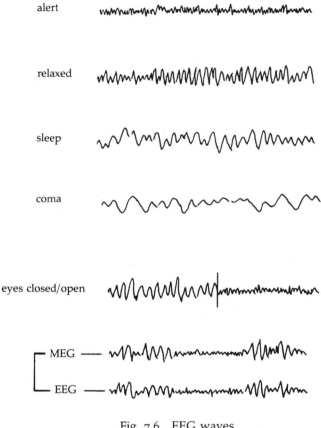

Fig. 7.6   EEG waves

Studying these patterns, it should be fairly clear to the more mathematically-minded that we are not dealing with simple waveforms below 30 Hz. The wavetrains are for the most part fairly irregular, and perhaps indicate combinations of higher frequencies. But they are not so irregular as to be random, and this would suggest higher frequencies not too far apart. If, for example, there are two vibrational centres of frequency 60 and 62 Hz, and total effect is a somewhat irregular oscillation of 61 Hz, together with a 'beating' effect of 2 – each beat in fact representing half a cycle of a 1 Hz waveform. To be mathematically precise, the combined waveform is the product of 'half-sum' and 'half-difference' frequencies. With the

EEG, we are clearly considering rather rough approximations to waveforms of a definite repetitive pattern and consistent frequency; and therefore an interpretation in terms of beat or difference frequency seems a reasonable possibility.

One possible interpretation of the EEG is of a central (pineal) frequency, say x Hz, together with frequencies of approximately (x − 11) and (x + 11) associated with the two frontal centres. This would produce a difference frequency in each hemisphere of 11 – an alpha frequency. And it would also produce a frequency between the two frontal oscillators of 22 – a beta frequency.

As to the value of x, the work on magnetic phosphenes in California suggests that it is in the order of 100 Hz – this being a sensitive frequency to use in these experiments. In my own experiments under hypnosis, the colours green and yellow clearly predominated. This would seem to suggest frequencies around lower C of 128 Hz, and so perhaps closely associated with the lowest trunk frequency. The link with Yoga ideas should be very obvious.

As to the inhibiting of the alpha waves when the eyes are open, this would seem to correlate with the fact that the pineal centre is only active when the environmental lighting is at a minimum. Opening the eyes stimulates the frontal centres and inhibits the posterior centre, thus giving the effect of cutting off the normal alpha activity. Presumably this is effected through the optic nerves.

Concerning the theta waves, they represent a far too indefinite category to be discussed in these terms. The one other area that must interest us is the 7–9 Hz range that people can deliberately induce by meditative or trance techniques – and where they are not consciously willed, they are probably indicative of some disorder. The general feeling among people who try to develop these unusual states is that they are first reducing frontal and autonomic activity, and then trying to tune in to some more universal vibration. Now it just so happens that a most basic low-frequency resonance of the earth's geomagnetic field is about 7.8 Hz – this being directly related to the circumference of the earth and the speed of electromagnetic transmission. Thus it would seem that this meditational process consists of inhibiting the beta waves, and trying to tune down the alpha waves towards the earth's vibration.

Overall, the concept of three specific oscillators would seem to account well with the main findings of EEG research. Everyone of course has their own specific patterns reflecting their unique structure and individuality. But this common denominator of brain activity that EEG researchers have patiently elucidated is intelligible – in terms of frequency, position, and function – by this association of three basic vibrations with the diencephalon.

To the neurophysiologist, who is essentially concerned with functional rather than structural forces, the EEG remains a mysterious phenomenon. Naturally he would seek to interpret these patterns in terms of the electrical functioning of groups of neurons, but he finds it difficult to understand why they are so pervasive and consistent over large areas of the cortex. What he can at least ascribe to is the notion that the alpha rhythms represent the 'idling' state of the brain machine; and knowing, moreover, that the alpha waves in animals disappear when the thalamus is removed, he would probably agree that these oscillations are centred in the diencephalon or upper brainstem rather than the cortex itself. Therefore it would seem a relatively short step to make in interpreting the EEG rhythms, not as specific functional patterns, but rather as structural energy for building and sustaining the whole cerebral complex of neurons.

In a very different field of speculation, the new biorhythm enthusiasts may find additional justification for their belief in the existence of three clear-cut cycles of energy related to mental, emotional, and physical modes. It is not unreasonable to believe that through these centres, we respond to the longer-term rhythms of the solar system, which gives us various peaks and troughs of energy throughout the year. The physical cycle is supposed to take about 23 days, the emotional 28 days, and the mental 33 days. Thus they are saying that, over and above the continuous and immediate balancing operation necessary for stability and health in its widest sense, there are more universal influences affecting us on a daily basis, and which can be consciously taken into account. This is of course a limited form of astrology. Presumably the tough and rather insensitive individual is unlikely to be much affected, whereas the sensitive and irrational person can be totally ruled by them. Others, however, who are both sensitive and rational may well come to the conclusion that it is better to be consciously aware of these subtle effects, and thus try to make allowances for them. We certainly observe all these attitudes in the emotional cycles of the female.

Closely associated with these centres are the optic and oculomotor nerves. The oculomotor nerve originates close to the pineal position, and controls four of the six muscles of the eye. These muscles, as stated previously, are derived from the three cerebral somites of the embryo. The optic nerve is more than just another cranial nerve – it is a major system in itself. The nerve tracts from the two eyes, each containing about half a million fibres, cross over in the region of the two frontal centres, and then proceed round the brain core to central and occipital areas. In multiple sclerosis, it is surely significant that both oculomotor and optic nerves are affected in the early stages, thus suggesting incorrect functioning of at least one of the three centres – presumably in terms of frequency, or intensity, or both. Because of the involvement of the oculomotor nerve in particular, and because the effects of the disease in the body are not generally asymmetrical, it is probably the pineal centre that is adversely affected. This would be consistent with Edgar Cayce's view that this condition comes about, not through any physical agency or virus, but through psychic disturbances associated with deep memory.

If we regard the brain as being generated and sustained by three major oscillatory centres whose vibrations act as carrier waves for psychic material, then this is all generally intelligible. Like the acupoints on the surface, the nerve cells are nodal points in the whole complex of vibrations, and connections between them are presumably established through affinities in frequency. When these major centres fail in some way – through physical injury, through exposure to dangerous frequencies, through psychic strain – then the structural field will change, causing first and foremost basic changes in nerve cells and axons. This then gives rise to the various physical effects in different cerebral conditions, such as failure of transmitter chemicals in myasthenia gravis and Parkinson's disease, or the destruction of the nerve sheaths in multiple sclerosis.

From observing physical injury to the brain, we are now well aware of the extreme sensitivity of the brain core, as opposed to the cortex. Small injuries to the thalamic region and upper brainstem can often be fatal, and brain death criteria are based on this region. By contrast, people can recover completely from serious injury to the cortex. The fact that there are some who function perfectly well on one hemisphere is now being used as an argument against the idea of asymmetrical development between right and left sides. However, this would seem more of a confirmation that the asymmetries have their origin in the brain core, and the hemispheres are suitably used according to the material available.

There is now considerable interest in the work of another pioneer of brain research, Karl Lashley, who spent a lifetime searching for the memory engram or record in the cellular structure of the brain. Eventually he saw this as a pointless quest, for it seemed to him that most of the cortex was relatively uncommitted to any specific functioning, and adaptable to whatever was required. In his view of the *equipotentiality* of the cortex, memories and perceptions were functions of large areas of the brain, rather than of particular neuron circuits.

In the light of surgical evidence, this is a very reasonable view. But we are beginning to wonder why man has developed such a large cortex if so little is absolutely necessary, and if it is only some peripheral adjunct to the vital functioning of the brain core. Perhaps the essential feature of the cortex is that it allows significant retention of the electrical stimuli prior to the organisation into long-term memory. The cortex may be regarded as, above all else, a short-term memory; and the reason why we are able to store so much experience and knowledge, compared with the limited abilities of animals, is that we have more temporary storage available for the multitude of inputs coming from all the sensory systems of the body.

This thought is related to the concept of the *specious present* much discussed by philosophers such as William James and Whitehead. This is the idea of a certain overlap from one moment to another, giving us both the sense of conscious continuity and natural change as we move forward in time. In scientific terms, its time content has been variously estimated as a small fraction of a second to several seconds. Practically, we are all aware of great variations in this, depending on what we are doing. From the cerebral frequencies postulated, one would expect a very minimal overlap of at least one cerebral cycle, or about 1/100th of a second; and we know of a visual continuity involving about 1/12th of a second fundamental to cinematograph and TV technology.

But envisaging the nerve sensations reverberating around the brain circuitry of the cortex in circumstances of deep emotional and mental involvement, we can understand in principle the variations in the perception of time. Presumably the longer the retention period in the cortex, the greater the chance of conscious memory links being established; and with the links established, we then have the ability to retrieve these memory patterns from some central psychic core, and replay or re-experience them through the cortical processes. It is above all our ability to retain the conscious present for sufficient length of time in the neural matter, and to compare with the immediate or long-term past, that gives the human mind its unique powers of analysis and synthesis.

Briefly summarising this discussion, many of the differing views do relate to the concept of three cerebral centres. The two forward centres, with their different frequencies and opposite rotations, produce a degree of asymmetry and opposite magnetic polarisations in the two hemispheres. The third centre is perhaps to be regarded as the integrator of the other two, and as tending to counteract the asymmetrical effects. Together, these centres are the foci of psychical functioning, leaving the cortex something like a scratch-pad that is generally available for the elaboration of whatever needs to be accomplished.

Through such a concept, we get some sense of the threefold nature of man as expressed in body, soul, and spirit. The lowest and least conscious centre regulates the physical autonomics; the central sub-conscious centre reflects the emotional tone; and the highest con-scious centre drives the whole organism. With such an understand-ing, we can then appreciate the two lower and frontal centres as essential entities in future human development, allowing for greater insight into the subconscious processes, and greater control over bodily functioning.

However, for purposes of research, it is preferable at this stage of our knowledge to concentrate on the structural aspects of the centres, thinking of them as something between mind and body. Through oscillatory energies, they generate electrochemical forms, while at the same time responding to mental intentions. The study of these forma-tive energies is a step that science, even materialist science, can now take. This is putting neurology on a different level in that we are not so much asking what a group of neurons are doing, but how they came into existence in the first place, and how they are so organised. This leads to a new set of questions, which may be more amenable to analysis and rationalisation than present ones.

From a functional aspect, computer analogies may be useful in expressing the essential problems, and also perhaps help us to see modern reductionism in a less disturbing way. In a complex system, there is little point in asking what some individual transistor is doing; but it is important to appreciate the major functional divisions that will use this and other transistors in many different ways. The com-puter software and hardware, or the neural circuits, are mechanisms through which the mind can express itself, albeit in rather limited ways, and do not in any way diminish its significance. The reduction-ist fear that people have is that the neural circuits *are* the mind, and that ultimately there can be no sense in postulating some separate entity controlling them. It leads to the view that there are only behaviour patterns – and yet what was the process that led to this view? Was it simply another level of behaviour?

An important feature of today's evolving science is a slow return to more commonsense mental concepts, and an acknowledgement of intuitive processes in the development of rational understanding. In Michael Polanyi's philosophy of *tacit* knowledge, "we know more than we can say". It is important that we are able to discuss ourselves in terms that do not contradict our intuitive and commonsense view of ourselves – a sentiment completely in accord with the views of Jean Fernel, the founder of modern physiology. Physiology is above all a commonsense, pragmatic study. It has no explicit rules or methods, except for the local guidelines of different specialisations. We find something to study, and then pursue it as deeply as we can, drawing on anything that may be available or relevant. Penfield, Sherrington, and Lashley worked from no dogmatic basis – they just did the best they could in a complex situation, and gradually built up the evidence. There are obvious things, and not so obvious things, and our commonsense guides us through the difficulties. Behaviour patterns and autonomic reflexes are not the slightest use in such evaluations. To deny the independence of the mental level is a negation of the scientific process itself.

8. Morphogenetic Patterns

Given that there is a certain ordering of frequency along the spine and in the cerebral area, and that these frequencies produce definite patterning effects, as demonstrated by cymatic experiments, we should be able to follow through such ideas with modern computational and graphical techniques. For these low-frequency effects, we must naturally return to classical theory of electromagnetic fields and waves. Mathematically, we need to formulate a developing energy pattern that is sufficiently complex and variable at the cellular level, while at the same time possessing an overall coherence for the growth of major systems. Certainly, such a field could only be achieved by an oscillatory organisation of many different frequencies continually in and out of phase with each other.

For those who have found the discussion of spinal and cerebral oscillators far too speculative, I would suggest an alternative, and simpler way of considering body frequency. This is by means of velocity of nerve conduction, which depends primarily on the axon diameter, and the myelin sheath surrounding it. In vertebrates, most conduction velocities are of the order of a few metres per second. Thus, for example, taking a typical velocity of 10 metres per second, and a 2 centimetre length of nerve axon, this could generate a cycle of activity working up to 500 Hz – such as might be found in the neck and hands. In fact, if we assume an approximately uniform velocity of conduction down the spine, and take into account the variable, yet ordered spacing between vertebral sections, we will obtain a table of frequencies similar to that of chapter 6 for the main part of the spine.

Thus between two consecutive spinal nerve junctions, there is a natural frequency of energy conduction determined by the geometry and the electrical sheathing parameters. Or looked at the other way round, the frequency – perhaps of genetic origin – determines the geometry and electrical parameters. Thus each vertebral section, with a major nerve junction on either side of it, would be the source of an electromagnetic oscillation. Together these oscillators would generate the principal component of the morphogenetic field – other parts of the organism being much less significant, especially in the earlier stages of growth.

So assuming a series of standing waves along the notochord, or spine, with frequency varying according to the geometrical and genetic characteristics, the main consideration for the physical scientist is how this vibrational energy disperses or falls away from the source. From the new superconducting magnetometers, we know the field is extremely weak on the surface of the body – at most about one millionth of the geomagnetic field. In electromagnetism, most natural fields, including that of the earth, have *dipole* characteristics. Such fields arise from oppositely polarised charges, or currents, or magnetic poles, and converge much more quickly than monopolar sources such as we have with single charges or with gravitation. Dipole fields vary inversely as the cube of the distance, rather than the square of the distance for single sources. Considering EEG and other physiological evidence in terms of classical electromagnetics, Paul Nunez has argued in a scholarly work that the major nerve structures of the brain, and also the axons in the spinal cord, create dipole fields.

In approaching such a problem mathematically, it is very much easier to work with field *potential* rather than with field strength. The reason is that this is a scalar quantity, and can be simply added to, or subtracted from, when calculating the total effect from all the sources. For a dipole field, the potential term varies inversely as the square of the distance; and the gradient, or rate of change with respect to distance, of the potential gives us the field strength. Having decided on the nature of the source, and of the energy dispersion, the total energy potential can be calculated at any point, and equipotential contours drawn – akin to those we see on maps and weather charts. Where the contours are close together, there is a high gradient of potential, and thus a high field strength.

Diagrammatically, the model used was based on figure 8.1. Mathematically, the standing waves along the axis can be defined by a potential function of the form:

$$\sin(2\pi f x / v).\cos(2\pi f t)$$

where 'f' is the frequency for each segment, and 'v' the velocity of propagation. For this particular problem, 'v' should relate to the nerve conduction velocity just discussed.

Each segment is then considered as a single source of energy dispersing dipole waveforms throughout the cellular material, and attenuating rapidly towards the surface of the body. For the pictures in this chapter, the potential function was based on the expression

$$\sin(2\pi f x / r v).\cos(2\pi f t)/r$$

which as 'r' increases, tends towards a dipole field, and produces the

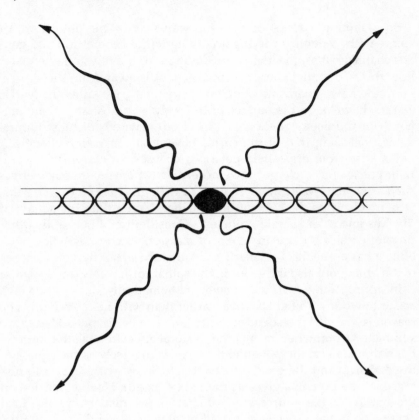

Fig. 8.1

type of decaying effect shown in the diagram, with the wavelength increasing towards the surface of the body. Other similar and related functions have been tried, but none have produced consistent patterning effects.

Figures 8.2 (a,b,c) are representative of some first attempts to model the morphogenetic field in this way, using just 5 trunk and 3 cerebral centres, and with relative frequency based on the discussion in chapter 5. The energy potential was calculated at each point on a surrounding grid, and a cumulative value derived over a given time period. From this, contours were generated at equal intervals of potential.

The three different time periods all show a characteristic division into head, thoracic, and abdominal regions, and might indicate that the relative frequencies are of the right order. One notes, as is to be expected, that different centres predominate at different times, and

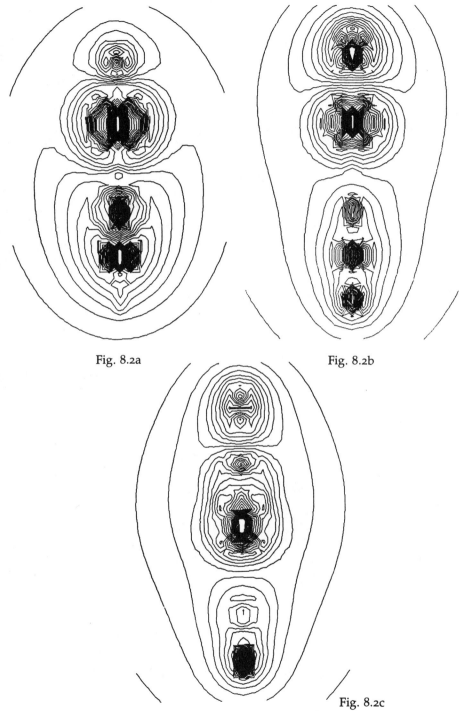

Fig. 8.2a

Fig. 8.2b

Fig. 8.2c

that the outer contours change in time around a basic oval form. Alternatively, considering these frequencies from a transverse viewpoint using the rotational methods of chapter 5, we obtain interesting spinal effects suggestive of the vertebral sections (figure 8.3).

From this simplified model, we are encouraged to proceed with the more detailed considerations suggested by table 6.2. Preliminary to this, we need first to investigate possible frequencies associated with the brainstem and cranial nerves, and for which there is little experimental evidence. Assuming there is an ordered sequence of frequency along the cerebrospinal axis, there are only three alternatives. Either the range is above the frequencies of the upper spine, or below those of the lower spine, or between the two. By introducing a new centre into the simplified model, and testing for the three alternatives, we see that only one of them produces a recognisable neck pattern (8.4c), this having a centre added below the lowest of the other frequencies. The two other options (8.4a,b) distort the overall form.

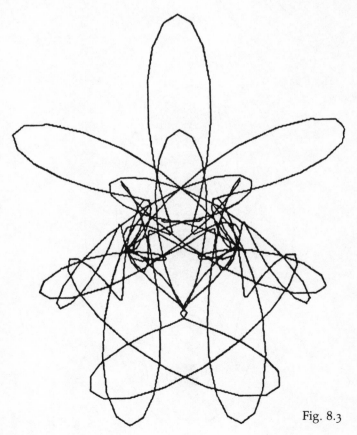

Fig. 8.3

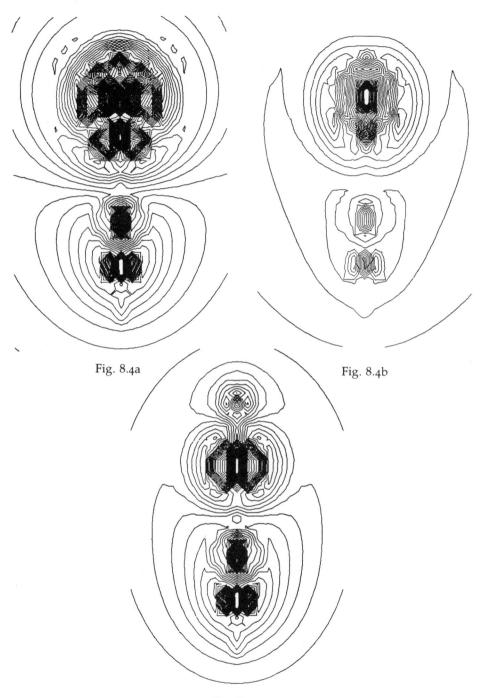

Fig. 8.4a

Fig. 8.4b

Fig. 8.4c

On general pragmatic grounds, this seems the most likely. If we are to assume, for instance, that the overall structuring is in anyway related to chromosome structuring, then we would expect an ordered sequence of frequency, without repetition. Also the basic discontinuity in the neck formation would seem to preclude a natural continuity of frequency from spine to brainstem. On such grounds, an ascending sequence from about 128 Hz in the base of the spine, followed by an ascending sequence in the brainstem up to the same level in the brain core, would give a unique set of frequencies, and an abrupt change from trunk to head.

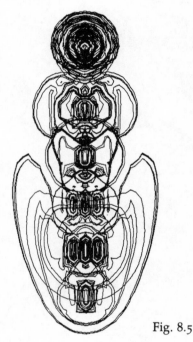

Fig. 8.5

Figure 8.5 is the last of the pictures with the simplified model. This was obtained by overlaying contour pictures at different timeintervals – although it could also be interpreted as involving higher harmonics. The main purpose of this form of output is to highlight those features that show a consistent patterning effect. Note that in such pictures, the closeness of the contours does not necessarily imply a high gradient, or field strength. This patterning technique was adopted for all the later work shown.

Moving on to the more detailed model involving 46 frequency centres, and using exactly the same methods, some typical results are shown in figures 8.6. For smaller time-intervals, the contouring gives a closed cellular form, with some suggestion of the further development. For longer time-intervals, there is an opening up, exposing head and pelvic formations, and very variable and complex patterns between. In the practical problem of getting interesting pictures, it should be remembered that most of the energy resides close to the central axis, with very much smaller energy levels for the remainder of the grid. Thus it is sensible to bias the contour selection a little towards the lower energy levels.

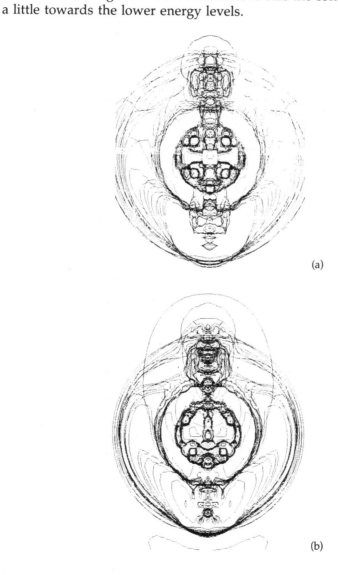

(a)

(b)

Fig. 8.6

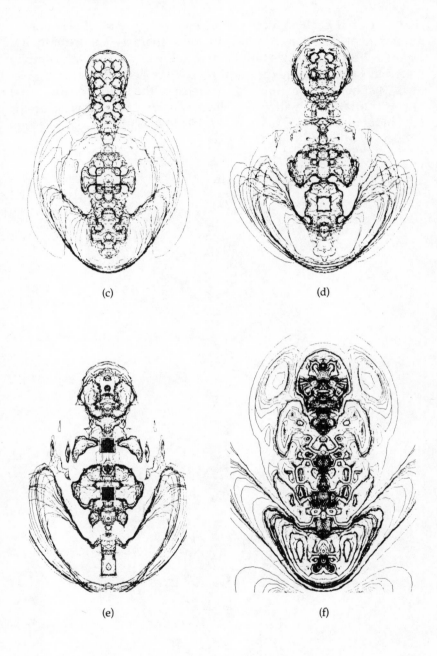

(c)

(d)

(e)

(f)

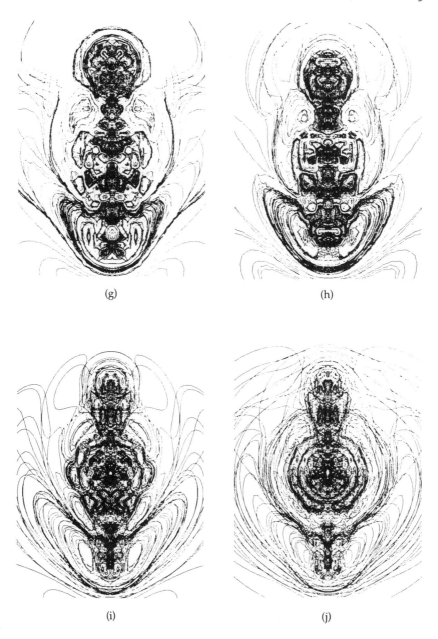

(g)

(h)

(i)

(j)

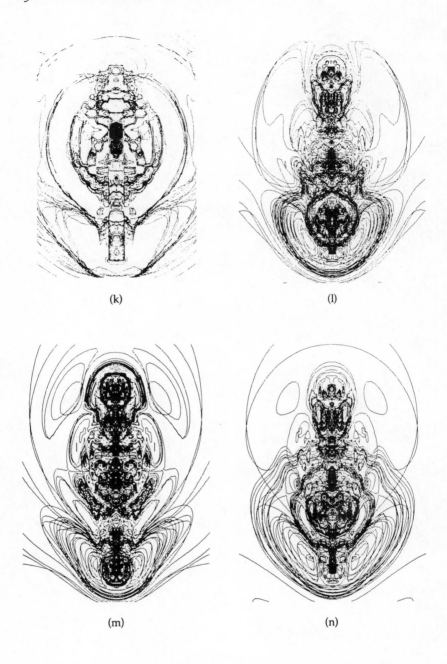

(k)

(l)

(m)

(n)

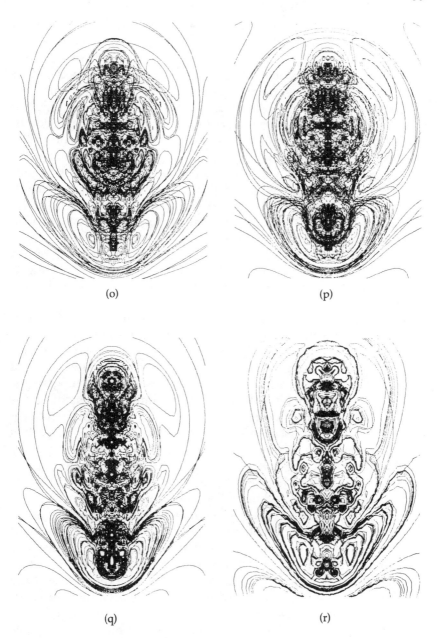

(o)

(p)

(q)

(r)

The effect of the velocity of conduction on these patterns is of interest. Taking approximate adult spine dimensions, and assuming a velocity of conduction of about 10 metres per second, the pictures shown are relatively stable within about 15% of this velocity. With higher velocities of conduction, the picture becomes gradually less differentiated, converging towards an elongated oval pattern. For lower velocities, the reverse happens, with far wider dispersion of energy from the central channel, and steady loss of cohesion in the patterning processes.

Of course it may be that some other type of energy distribution, with different frequencies, could produce more convincing effects. One cannot assert that the various assumptions made are directly validated by the pictures. But they do at least confirm the general idea that *it is possible* that the cellular material of the body is patterned by means of electromagnetic waveforms with a definite ordering of frequency along the central axis. Therefore it seems well worth trying to make detailed frequency measurements within the body with such assumptions in mind.

Whatever the correct mathematical formulation, it is clear that in the field and vibrational approach, there is a definite prospect of coming to a basic understanding of form and structure in the physical body. If our reasoning is correct, then beneath the outer physical appearance of things, there exists a composite and homogeneous system that, on the one hand, generates the infinite variety of physical effects; and on the other hand, coordinates with the psychical aspects of mind, emotion, instinct and sexual activity. Putting this slightly differently, we might say that, from a common frequency pattern, there is on the one side the same basic physiology common to all life; and on the other, the endless diversity between individuals through interaction with differently evolved psychical forms.

This is more than just a very general idea – such as we have in the DNA-theorising about a chemical code determining all aspects of form. It is, as we see, something that we can begin to evaluate mathematically – a concept clearly grasped in their very different ways by both Alan Turing and Hans Jenny. In observing complex and changing physical forms, it is so easy to miss the underlying oscillatory and polarising forces. Yet once these have been brought to our rational consciousness, the development of everything in the organic world becomes generally intelligible.

The problem with all purely particle theories, both at the atomic and organic levels, is that they seem to imply an indefinite causal regression. If, for instance, the genes are the determining particle factors for organic structure, then what are the particle factors that structure the genes – and so on. Rupert Sheldrake has recently expressed very clearly the difficulties of accepting the DNA thesis as it now stands. His own alternative is to suggest that organic form is determined by *morphic resonance* with the past.

According to this viewpoint, once a certain form, or even a behaviour pattern, comes into being, it somehow impresses itself on all similar patterning processes, reinforcing itself with each repetition. Thus, independent of space and time constraints, each species settles down into its own groove, so to speak. In direct support of such a theory, he points out that once laboratory animals are taught a certain trick in one place, others of the species often show the same ability very soon afterwards in some other part of the world.

Just how morphic resonance operates, he does not venture to speculate. But in pluralist terms of a 'field' or psychical entity that contains the memory of its own evolution, or in terms of some earth or cosmic memory, then such a theory is generally intelligible. However, as he is careful to point out, this is a non-energetic theory of morphogenesis, and so can in no way explain the particular physical forces that directly mould the cellular material.

The main objection by biologists to any electromagnetic theory of morphogenesis is that the energy fields are only the result of chemical organisation, and not in any sense *formative*. This *passive* view of electromagnetics misses the point. Take, for instance, the connection of a condenser and magnetic coil which form the standard tuned circuit. Without any field considerations, the condenser would just discharge through the coil, and that would be the end of electrical activity. But an *active* field comes into play, and this reacts back on the coil to charge up the other side of the condenser, and so on. The oscillation is very much the result of the field, which changes the whole nature of the energy activity. In the more complex dynamics of the body where chemicals are continually rearranging themselves, matter and field respond and resonate together, and must at least be considered mutually interdependent.

The analytical methods used in this chapter should be thought of as a preliminary study prior to any attack on the major problems of embryology. From our obviously idealised model, we move on to try to conceive how the controlling oscillators develop from the fertilised ovum, and how the field and genetic energies continually expand to form more complex versions of the original inherent organisation. At this stage of our knowledge, I would venture just a few brief thoughts and ideas in this area.

A basic initial point to be made, and on which there would be little controversy, is that the function of each cell depends on its relative position in the body – relative both to the overall geometry, and to the localised organisation of cells. More specifically, the DNA processes in the nucleus of each cell are activated or inhibited according to the localised field forces derived from the whole structure. Thus we get a selective activation of genes, or DNA sequences, or oscillatory energies, and this activation tends to reinforce the field in the region of the cell.

Now from the first cell – and in fact from all cells with the double-chromosome content in the nucleus (*diploid* cells) – there is the potentiality for a complete vertebrate structure. Let us assume then that this original cell is totally active in the beginning, with all the oscillators functioning along the lines of the complete system as modelled in this chapter.

After the first division, there is a basic change of relation of cell to field, each cell's activity not only reacting to its own field, but being influenced by the field of the other. Thus the genes of each will be differently activated from those of the original cell. Then as further cellular divisions occur, the outer cells will become more selective in their action, while the inner ones, although selective to some extent, would function more like the original cell. In other words, there would be a 'gradient' of selectivity from inner to outer, and thus something equivalent to the embryological categories of endoderm, mesoderm, and ectoderm.

Such a process I suggest would tend to create an organisation that reflects the form of the original field, only with immensely more detailed variety due to the cumulative action of all the individual cells differently activated. And in particular, the notochord, then the somites, then the vertebral column, would gradually become the counterparts of the original nuclear material.

Therefore on this basis, and assuming there are dominant frequencies associated with the chromosomal segments, the spinal cord and brainstem would section out in a similar way, and the cells in each section would resonate with the dominant field frequency in that region. This would be a mutual effect, with field and nuclear material suitably reinforcing each other at a particular frequency, and tending to filter out other frequencies.

In my opinion, such a conception could now be tested out in an elementary way by mathematical methods, although requiring the most extensive computational facilities. As a minimum, there is the possibility of considering field-cellular interactions for a few divisions, and investigating whether or not this gives something resembling the first primitive stages of cellular organisation.

There is today a new branch of structural engineering – finite element analysis – which might be adapted for this purpose. In the finite-element approach, material structures are subdivided mathematically into a large number of small elements, and the effects of external forces and vibrations are evaluated by solving the simultaneous equations of motion for all the separate elements. The total cumulative effect over a period is gradually built up from computations done at many discrete points of time. Such techniques are also used in problems of hydrodynamics.

With cellular elements, there are the added problems that each is a dynamic source of energy, and divides into two every so often. Thus the embryological problems would be that much more complex. For inert structural problems, the calculations sometimes take days to complete on the fastest machines. We therefore have to be prepared for massive quantities of computational time.

But this is a challenge, and I would expect the physical-science laboratories of major universities to be more than anxious to follow this line of thought through. For so long now, they have looked on rather helplessly while biochemists imagined that they would one day solve the problems of organic structure.

9. Electromagnetic Studies

After more than half a century of deliberate avoidance of electromagnetics, there is now some recognition within the biological schools that electromagnetism must play a significant part in organic development. There are just too many obvious effects involving currents, and fields, and potentials, for this factor to be overlooked any longer. For instance, there is not the slightest doubt that regeneration of limbs in simpler forms of life does depend critically on current and potential, and these can be artificially applied to induce successful regeneration. Such ideas are once again being used to speed up the repair of bone fractures in humans – this being a common form of treatment in the nineteenth century.

But we are moving on from this, and using more subtle *field* energies from low-frequency coils to heal and strengthen bones. And to give more concentrated energy input, some are using much higher frequency fields, only pulsed at low frequencies. These two methods seem to produce similar effects in organic tissue. Cancerous growths are also being treated in this way – this again being a version of nineteenth century practice based on the idea that most tumours generate unusual electrical potentials.

Such matters have been fairly well reported in articles and on television, and have been carefully written about by researchers such as R. O. Becker. In this chapter, I will not attempt to go over this ground, but will rather consider some ideas and studies that may be less familiar, and which link up with other parts of this book. At the back of our mind should be the thought that, without any theoretical postulates to work from, practical research and medical therapy in this field must inevitably be rather hit and miss.

Low-frequency electromagnetics is now coming into cellular studies. For the last two or three decades, the accent has been on the biochemistry of the nucleus, and the synthesis of proteins through DNA control mechanisms. But attention is now beginning to focus as much on the outer domains of the cell, the *cytoplasm*, and in particular on the structure and role of the membrane, which gives the impression of having a life of its own, separate from the genetic material of the nucleus, and responding in remarkable ways to the cellular environment. Researchers have discovered that certain molecules in the membrane are highly responsive to low-frequency magnetic fields, and that the membrane as a whole acts, in technical jargon, as a 'low-pass filter'. Some are of the opinion that, within the very narrow temperature range of the body, the membrane is *superconductive* – a term normally applying only to extremely low temperatures.

There is new thinking too in brain cell communication. Theories based on slow-wave field activity affecting membranes and dendrites are competing with more conventional ideas of transmission from cell to cell along the axon. In this context, the EEG patterns of the brain are regarded not just as the peripheral residual noise of electrical energy, but as something that can actually drive the brain, and determine its state of consciousness. For example, if a radio wave is suitably pulsed or modulated at the very slow delta wave frequencies of 2 or 3 cycles per second then, when directed at animals or humans, a type of sleep state can quickly follow. In a recent paper in *Magnetic Field Effects on Biological Systems*, the American scientist, W. R. Adey points out the very close correspondence, frequency-by-frequency, between the EEG and the neuronal wave, thus suggesting the pervasiveness of the slow-wave electromagnetics throughout the brain. In a concluding comment, he states:

... there are apparently special structural organisations in the central nervous system of all vertebrates and particularly the mammal, which may make him susceptible in very subtle ways to the environmental electric fields, electromagnetic fields, and to the intrinsic fields in brain tissue.

More detailed studies of the electrical transmission along the nerve axon, involving waveforms of sodium and potassium ions, are beginning to incorporate the newly developing science of *solitons*. A soliton is a cohesive waveform (fluid, electromagnetic, etc.) that can travel through a medium with particle-like properties of movement and interaction with other solitons. This new science, with its precise mathematical formulation, is being used both in particle physics and physiology. Certainly the nerve impulse has the basic properties of a soliton.

Entirely new types of measurement and diagnostic procedures for cerebral processes and abnormalities are coming into research and clinical work. For example, the new superconducting magnetometers can provide much more specific information than older methods based on the electroencephalogram (EEG) which has always been complicated to set up and use. The magnetoencephalogram (MEG) does not depend on contact with the skull, which is transparent to the magnetic fields of the brain, and one can determine in 3-dimensions the precise focus of a disturbance in a way that is not possible with the EEG. This has now been successfully used in localising epileptic seizures in the temporal region of the brain, and for following the energy effects in other regions, including the opposite cortex.

The low-frequency magnetic environment of the body does help us to resolve in a general way many of the problems connected with the human aura. Scientists have found very little evidence of the emission of light-frequency photons from the body – although with the most sensitive instruments, some electromagnetic energy of this nature can just be detected. But as has been indicated earlier, low-frequency magnetism can be 'seen' as colour patterns in a light hypnotic state – and with the eyes closed. In this situation, it is natural to assume that the magnetic field is directly activating some part of the nervous system involved in the interpretation of colour. However, as only a few people see auras all the time, as rather more can see them under particular lighting conditions or with special concentration, and as most do not see anything at all in the normal waking state, one must conclude that the field energies are of such intensity as to be right on the borderline of human perception. It requires either an internal boosting of the signal strengths, or a very selective focussing and removal of unhelpful environmental noise, or a definite change of cerebral state, to bring them to the level of a conscious visual experience. Direct measurement of the field strengths tends to confirm this viewpoint.

What we do definitely know in scientific terms is that the waking self does respond to high-intensity magnetic fields in the cerebral range of about 10–100 cycles per second. These produce sensations of light and colour around the head, as with very low-intensity fields under hypnosis. Those researching these magnetic phosphene effects are inclined to the view that the field is activating the retina rather than directly inducing currents in the optic nerve – although there is the possibility that, through the major cerebral centres, an entirely different perceptual level is involved. But whatever the reason, this causal explanation of the aura in terms of low-frequency electromagnetics is consistent with all the evidence, and provides a definite theoretical basis for further research into the subject.

Electromagnetic ideas also help to rationalise the varied and apparently conflicting views about the basic concepts of acupuncture. After writing several books explaining traditional theory, Felix Mann caused some consternation by coming to the conclusion that acupoints and meridians were 'imaginary' concepts – although recognising that it is difficult to distinguish the real and imaginary in physics. But if this were the case, how do we account for the specific conductive properties of acupoints? Anyone can find these points electrically, and neurophysiologists have to assume that at these points there must exist a high concentration of nerve ganglia just under the skin. Some researchers will accept the acupoint as 'real', yet discount the meridian – apart from a certain usefulness in categorising similar effects. Some think of the meridians in terms of pain channels, corresponding in part to recognised pathways along which pain sensations tend to travel.

All views receive a degree of recognition in terms of an 'imaging' biofield of oscillatory energy, whose physical effect is electromagnetic. In these terms, the acupoints are those nodal regions where the low-frequency energy comes to a small and fairly consistent peak. As would be expected, and as acupuncturists know, their position on the surface of the skin does slightly vary from day to day. To each of these nodes, there will be a certain basic frequency, or several related frequencies in natural resonance. Thus, when one is stimulated, others with similar vibrational modes will also be affected. So we obtain a more subtle concept of a meridian – not so much as a simple linear flow of energy, but rather as a chain of related oscillators sensitive to each other. In these terms, a meridian is about as real, or imaginary, as a line of force, or an equipotential contour. As for the practice of traditional acupuncture, it may be more relevant to consider this as a triggering impulse for the electrical oscillators rather than as a direct stimulation of the nerves.

In clinical terms, one can envisage distortion of the oscillatory fields emerging in many different ways, from schizophrenia to cancer, from memory failure to the common cold. Some of the most serious and intractable problems involve nerve degeneration and subsequent paralysis, and orthodox medical science sees little hope of any solution. The nerve axon may slowly grow again from the nerve cell after being damaged or severed, but if it does not find its natural connections fairly quickly, it will not resume its natural functions. More primitive vertebrates can recover much better; but in the mammal, there seem to be many cellular obstructions in the reforming of nerve connections. Where neurotransmitters seem to be failing, like dopamine for Parkinson's disease, chemical input can be of some help in restoring natural function. But as with cortisone input, it is impossible to direct the precise amounts at the precise time to precise areas, and the mental and physical side-effects can become as significant as the original condition.

Alternative systems of medicine that claim to work directly on the structural body of forces deny that there are any incurable conditions. By reinforcing the natural vibratory forces within the body, they are convinced all is curable. Unfortunately, the idea that specific tissues and systems may require specific frequency patterns is not yet part of the present medical consciousness. So much experimentation is done, even in the mapping of the brain, where frequency of input is of no consideration. So few seem to realise, for instance, that whereas 100 volts can be lethal at 60 Hz, many thousands of volts can be quite harmless at a higher frequency. Yet Nikola Tesla explored these matters nearly a century ago, and discovered much about both earth and body resonance. The time has surely come to develop his work further, and tune in to the natural rhythms of the body. In such a way, it is possible that we will find very specific remedies for some of the more intractable conditions of modern medicine.

In pure research, the concept of organic development being controlled through electromagnetic field patterns leads to many new ideas. For example, one very intriguing biochemical problem is the fact that all 'living' molecules possess a certain type of asymmetry, whereas those produced in the laboratory are generally mixtures of two complementary forms that, overall, are statistically symmetrical.

The geometrical and optical asymmetry of molecules is the basic concern of *stereochemistry*. The central fact in this specialisation is that, when the carbon atom is linked in a tetrahedral way to four different atoms – as is most common in organic material – two geometrically different molecules can be produced which are the mirror image of each other. The usual way to distinguish one from the other is by the effect of polarised light, which is rotated to the right with one molecule (*Dextrorotatory*), and to the left with its mirror image (*Laevorotatory*). In the body, all the main amino acids, which are the building blocks for protein, exist only in the L-form; and in fact, all potentially asymmetrical molecules are specifically of one form. Although containing the same atomic ingredients, the separate forms may have different effects on the senses, with for instance, one tasting sweet and the other bitter, or one having a pleasant smell and the other quite odious. Latest immunological work in this area suggests that the body may attack one form of the molecule but not the other.

From a purely biochemical viewpoint, this polarisation of molecules has been a puzzling matter. However, we know that magnetic fields can control such polarisation; and either in terms of the body fields, or the earth's field, or both, there is a plausible electromagnetic answer to this question.

The importance of the electromagnetic bonding forces in organic processes is now clearly recognised by all life-scientists and therapists. Through, for instance, the single, double, and triple phosphate bonds, the cells store and release energy as required; and through the double helix bonding, the genetic material of the nucleus is replicated in cell division. Biochemistry and allopathic medicine concentrate on the molecular level of bonding, while esotericists of various schools attempt to conceive the total integrated field of electromagnetic vibration. The homoeopathic school, in particular, understands the importance of low-frequency energy in therapeutic work – while warning allopaths of the dangers of high-frequency methods that damage molecular and genetic bonding. In their curious *potentising* processes of mechanical vibration and almost infinite dilution, they seem to carry these ideas beyond all rationality. However, those who have tried some of these preparations will know how effective the results can be. Try, for instance, a few sips of a plantain leaf dilution for the numbing of gums – in which hardly a single molecule of the original remains.

We must assume that the homoeopath is trying to extricate from the complex maze of particles certain specific vibrational energies. These presumably relate back to the electromagnetic bonding forces of the dissolved substance, and also to the basic bonding forces of water itself, these being sensitive to weak low-frequency electromagnetic fields. In water, through the positive H and negative OH ions, there is a most subtle balance of acid/alkaline, or Yin/Yang forces; and as about 65% of the body is water, this balance is likely to have a most significant effect on body processes and functions. So, while the 'homoeopathic dose' is only a placebo in orthodox chemical terms, in terms of the low-frequency electromagnetics of the body, together with the specific properties of water, we begin to grasp something much more significant about this type of treatment. And on a larger scale, the very creation of primitive life-forms may be controlled through the interaction of the earth's electromagnetic field and water.

Diverse geomagnetic studies do seem to be moving towards such a conclusion. Fortunately, this area of research has been brought together in a classic text *The Geomagnetic Field and Life* by the Russian scientist Aleksandr Dubrov. This is a major work of synthesis, involving detailed argument from physics, physiology, and medicine. It combines Western studies with extensive research in Eastern Europe over the last twenty-odd years, and provides general support for the field and resonance concepts of this book.

Venturing far beyond the experimental detail, he propounds a new version of evolutionary theory in which all living forms develop, not randomly through chance mutations, but through definite causal processes resulting from the interaction with the varying forces, resonances, and polarities of the environmental geomagnetic field

(GMF). Very major changes in species occur in periods of reversal of the field, while fairly continuous change is brought about by more localised disturbances. He regards the moment at which an organism begins to grow, and the specific interaction of genetic and molecular polarities with GMF polarities, as of fundamental importance to its future development. The geomagnetic forces are essentially life-giving, while the complementary gravitational forces stabilise these effects.

In experiments on the relationship of the GMF to living organisms, Dubrov concentrates on three major techniques that have been used. The first is that of screening out as far as possible all GMF effects in special cages; the second is that of compensating with magnetic coils for the GMF, and making artificial changes in magnetic north-south directions; and the third is to follow the intrinsic or circadian rhythms (blood, hormone, EEG, ECG, cell division, excretion, etc.) of organisms, and compare them with fluctuations in GMF activity.

The latter method does of course require the existence of a number of 'magnetic observatories' following the fluctuations of the field right through each day and year. And they also have to follow the course of each of the main components of the field as well.

Thus it is necessary to distinguish the comparatively static component from the low-frequency oscillations occurring between the ionosphere and the earth's surface (basic frequencies of 7.8, 14.1, 20.3 Hz). Comparison must sometimes be made with the specific horizontal or vertical components, or just to the gradient between them – the Dip. Over and above these, there is the Interplanetary Magnetic Field (IMF) arising mainly from the sun. This itself is fluctuating according to the 27-day period of rotation of the sun, and according to changes of sun-spot activity and polarity.

Figure 9.1 shows the general form of the earth's magnetic aura. The stream of solar particles are slowed down by interaction with the geomagnetic field, and a standing shock wave is created within it. The subsequent cavity formed within the solar stream is called the *magnetosphere*, and its outer boundary the *magnetopause*. On the night side of the earth, there is a long comet-like tail, with concentrated electromagnetic activity along the 'spinal' axis where the lines of force change direction from one side to the other. Closer to the earth are the special Van Allen radiation belts, with high-energy particles trapped by the magnetic forces.

Concerning shielded experiments, in which the geomagnetic field is largely excluded by the use of special alloys, cells, microorganisms, plants and animals, all tend to show a lowering of vital activity. In one particular experiment, mice became weak and inactive, spending

a lot of their time on their backs; and by the fourth generation, repro-
duction had ceased. Both the skin and internal organs showed considerable morphological change. With man, such as those screened
for long periods in submarines, metabolism is lowered and basic
rhythms altered, leading sometimes to morbid states. Similar effects
occur in deep-space conditions.

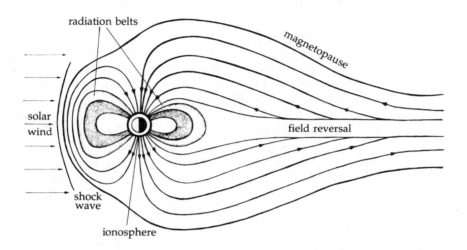

Fig. 9.1   Geomagnetic field

In compensated-field experiments, one has to remember that, in
general, only the comparatively static element of the field is artificially
reproduced. Many of these experiments are directional in nature,
such as with birds and fish, to try to discover their natural naviga-
tional mechanisms. While there are some positive results, many are
inconclusive. But this is not surprising according to our analysis, as
the cerebral systems would be most likely to respond to the low-
frequency resonances – one of these being about the alpha-frequency
level. An important point to emerge from these experiments is that
living forms seem to respond most positively to field intensities about
those of the GMF (approx. 0.5 gauss). For bird navigation, it would
seem we have to get both intensity and frequency of the right order.

GMF techniques have been used to study certain chemical reac-
tions whose variable, and sometimes irreproducible, nature represents a considerable challenge to orthodox theory. For instance, both
colloidal suspensions, and crystallisation processes are affected by
low-frequency GMF energies, and crystals tend to orient themselves

according to the local field. One naturally assumes that this is relevant to the colloidal nature of protoplasm, and to crystal structures in the cell membrane.

As to how many of these effects are mediated, Dubrov comes to much the same conclusion as several other researchers, and as previously discussed. The two main candidates are: (a) the polarisation and ionisation of the water molecule; (b) the electromagnetic properties of the cell membrane, particularly the magnetic permeability. He also notes that we are slowly beginning to map the intrinsic magnetic field of organisms, and that we may find more direct relationships this way. In this respect, he conceives the acupoints and meridian system as part of the magnetic structure and polarisation through which the GMF acts on the body. This being so, it might suggest that the traditional methods using magnetisable needles are the most effective.

The main substance of Dubrov's evolutionary concepts involves consideration of symmetry and asymmetry in living forms. As previously mentioned, all organic molecules that are inherently asymmetric take exclusively either the L or D form, not both. Such *dissymmetry* (a specific form of asymmetry) is directly related to a magnetic property concerning the polarisation of light through the molecule. However, this is only one aspect of asymmetry, Dubrov considering the left-handed, right-handed, and symmetric characteristics of the genes themselves, which produce polarisations of function and structure up to the highest levels of the organism – and as we are consciously aware in our own movements.

There is microscopic and macroscopic evidence relating these polarities to the GMF. Through some very complex biochemical work, basic polarisation changes of the gene and chromosome structure of the fruit-fly have shown a close correlation with localised field disturbances. At the other extreme, there is growing evidence to support the sensible thesis that, during a reversal of GMF polarity (about every half-million years), the more dissymmetric of species are the most adversely affected. However, such reversals are comparatively slow compared with species life, and involve lower field strengths. Thus some adaptation to the new polarities seems possible.

According to Dubrov, the geomagnetic field is the primary factor determining the asymmetry or symmetry of organisms. Various plants have been shown to have different growth forms according to whether the seeds are oriented towards the north or south magnetic poles. This we are told also applies to higher organisms, with the head of the female embryo naturally gravitating towards the south, and the male towards the north. Predominance of sympathetic nervous activity, or of parasympathetic activity during the day is also a form of polarity, and both effects are accentuated during periods of magnetic storms.

Opposite responses to the same physical factor are found in most organic processes, and this inversion is supposedly due to the role of the GMF in the formation of the response. What is left-handed, or right-handed, or symmetric, whether in structure or function, varies throughout each individual, and is conditioned according to the field structure at the beginning of life. The complex nature of the geomagnetic polarities, with basic changes from morning to evening, through ionospheric resonances, through the varying patterns of the IMF, ensures infinite variety of polarised forms.

He discusses the possible *biosuperconductivity* of cell membranes referred to earlier. In the very low temperature superconductivity of physics, it is possible to register the most minute changes of magnetic field. Dubrov points out that dowsers show sensitivity to fields of the order of 10^{-14} gauss, even greater than that of modern magnetometers based on superconductivity. This would suggest some comparable process, associated with cell membranes, which only takes place within a very small temperature range: 2 or 3 degrees above or below this brings most activity in the body to a halt.

At a more detailed level, Dubrov discusses these matters in terms of magnetic spin, and with some conjecture on the possible existence of a second gravitational vector interacting with the magnetic vector (chapter 4). Polarity, symmetry, and asymmetry are dealt with geometrically, involving translation, rotation, and mirror reflection. Through such transformations, he sees the possibility of a theoretical understanding of various element transmutations that seem to take place in biological systems, such as magnesium to calcium, carbon to magnesium, etc. In fact, he points out that the entire periodic table of elements can now be understood in terms of geometrical mirror symmetry.

Dubrov refers to many medical papers relating disease and disorder to magnetic disturbance. The principal effect seems to be on the blood, with, for instance, decreased hemoglobin counts, decreased adrenalin levels, and more heart attacks with increased activity of the GMF. Also under such conditions, smallpox, dysentery, tetanus, and many other matters were made worse. Concerning cerebral and mental disorder, increase of GMF disturbance relates to an increase in neuroses and general level of accidents, but tends to decrease the number of epileptic fits. There is also some evidence that organisms like herpes, which may be dormant for years, can suddenly be activated by the GMF. Dubrov concludes that:

Geomagnetobiology has now taken its first steady steps, confirming by experiment and observation that "life came into being and has evolved in the presence of the geomagnetic field." . . . Geomagnetobiology has laid firm new bases for a study of biological rhythmicity, and opens up great opportunities for the further development of natural scientific disciplines; in this lies its importance as a science of the future.

Dubrov's thesis suggests an evolutionary approach that, in my view, is more plausible than the random mutation theory of neo-Darwinism. The intrinsic genetic factors respond to the energy fields of the earth, which in turn respond to those of the sun and cosmos generally. These are not isolated processes, but part of an intelligible order. Only in this strangely myopic and specialised age could it be assumed that we are not related to the external order of things.

To conclude this chapter, I will briefly comment on my own simple experimentation over the last few years, which required no complex laboratory equipment. It involved a home-made audio-oscillator, with electric probe and magnetic coil that could be used separately or together. The probe easily registers the cerebral acupoints, and surprisingly, I found the coil just sensitive to my own field. The probe can be used for direct electrical input to the body, and the coil used to demonstrate magnetic phosphenes around the head.

In applying audio-frequency energies to the body, there is at the outset a very basic decision to be made about the type of waveform to be used. Most therapists have the impression that it is unwise to apply a pure tone of a precise frequency – this would be too extreme, too specific in its effect. In all forms of treatment, whether by a single chemical, or a single colour, or through a single meridian, other things tend to get out of balance. The therapist has a similar problem to that of the artist or the composer – our senses have to be pushed this way and that in order to create a harmonious whole. One possible technological solution to this is to generate a square waveform that contains, theoretically, an infinity of odd harmonics. Thus for instance, the note C would have compensating tones of G and E in higher octaves. In preference to the pure sine wave, such an input would at least seem a wise precautionary measure.

In my own experimental work, I used a simple square-wave circuit, as shown below (figure 9.2), with suitably large resistances for comparing with skin resistances, and giving frequencies over the whole audio range and beyond. By placing two points of the body across the resistors A or B, or across the capacitor C, the pitch of the output note significantly changes if the body resistance is unusually low. The normal technique for doing this is to hold a conducting cylinder in one hand, and to move the other terminal (acupoint detector A.D.)

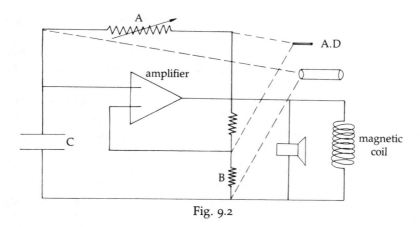

Fig. 9.2

across the skin until one finds a sudden change in the output frequency. If the resistance A is used, more current passes through the body than using B, and a small electric shock will be experienced on many acupoints around the head. However, for acupoint detection by frequency alone, the resistance B is the more sensitive.

Not everyone finds this immediately convincing. Skin resistance experiments can produce curious results for a number of reasons. These concern the state of the body, whether moist, sweaty, cold, dry, etc., the state of the atmosphere, particularly its electrical state dependent on the weather, and the type of heating or air conditioning. Thus, experimentation consistent in one environment over a period of time may appear inconsistent in another. And to further complicate matters, one's own emotional state does seem to affect the results. Some days the frequency may change up to an octave on some points; on another, perhaps by a third. However, in very general terms, it can be stated with some confidence that the normal body resistance of something in the order of a million ohms reduces to only a few thousand ohms between the acupoints.

Another interesting line of investigation involves using the oscillator directly on the spinal channel, placing one terminal near the base of the spine, with the other either on one of the cerebral acupoints, or just held in the hand. The first thing one finds is that, using resistance A, the output note rises anything up to about three octaves, thus indicating an extremely low resistance path of a few hundred ohms. In doing this, there is often a chromatic effect, with the note rising about one semitone on each breath. As the resistance A varies inversely with the frequency of the output note, this may represent indirect evidence for some chromatic ordering of frequency in the spine.

Attempting to use the oscillator for clinical conditions, one either works through dermatome charts and associated spinal segments, or through the acupuncture tradition, or just tries things on an intuitive basis. Concerning the latter, I have on at least three occasions brought on a heavy cold condition when experimenting on the face; and once I was able to transform a head cold to a very dry condition in the throat by joining the triple-warmer point near the eye to the central occipital point at the back of the head. My impression is that these were frequency-dependent effects.

There is much to suggest that vibrational treatments are best performed with the patient in a sleeping or hypnotic state, when the body is more open to low-frequency electromagnetism. The conscious self seems able to screen out unwanted energies to a remarkably high degree – as suggested by Eileen Garrett, and well illustrated by the magnetic phosphenes of light and colour to which the hypnotic subject is very sensitive, but requiring fields of several hundred gauss before they can be sensed by the waking mind. This is reminiscent of Reich's 'armouring' concept, involving the development of a rugged psychical shield screening out all unwanted material. Few of us can remain 'open' to all vibrations – it is too painful and too difficult. But in sleep or trance, it would seem that we lose most of this shielding, and are able to absorb more low-frequency energy.

So it is no surprise to find that a small magnetic coil can produce significant physical effects in the trance state. Even when held a few inches from the body, it can cause quite violent muscle spasms right down one side of the body. This would seem to indicate that magnetic forces are a basic factor in muscle movement, and not just some secondary effect.

Another interesting line of experimentation with the oscillator concerns the ionisation of water. Replacing the iron solenoid with a helical coil of thick wire inserted in a glass of water, and ionising the water according to a specific frequency, one can attempt to assess the physiological effects of different energy notes. This obviously has to be done over a long period of time, and preferably each night. My own experiments along these lines led me to suspect that certain frequencies adversely affected my sleep state, and also that they produced mild cold effects for a few hours the next morning. Other frequencies induced a state of general well-being. In fact, these experiments corresponded quite closely with those of attempting to cure head colds with the magnetic coil at a specific frequency. Frequencies around C seemed beneficial, while those about F or G seemed to make matters worse. In putting this down, I am not trying to make any objective statement, but hoping to encourage others to experiment along these lines.

Designing experiments to evaluate frequency-dependent effects – in the sense that the effect of C, say, is opposite to that of F – is extremely difficult with any living organism. For this reason, there is much to be said, in general therapeutic work, for using the oscillator on the spinal channel, and allowing it to move up naturally through several octaves, eventually finding its own upper level. My own experience suggests that this is a beneficial and balancing operation, without adverse side-effects.

There is a danger that, keeping to Western physiological models and clinical categories, vibrational treatment could get as complex as drug therapies now are. Each organ, although associated with certain dominant frequencies, develops in a great maze of electromagnetic rhythms, and sorting out just what it lacks is extremely difficult. But if we can comprehend the field frequencies in terms of a subtle anatomy of force-centres – as modelled in the computer graphics – then a new clinical approach could evolve. An earlier generation of researchers began to think on these lines, even envisaging a time would come when disease would be classified by wavelength, and the treatment become a mathematical certainty. This may be too simplistic a view, particularly with the recognition that the mind can block almost any sort of treatment. But it represents a rational and humane way forward, away from the unfortunate extremes of allopathy.

As vibrational and electromagnetic concepts evolve in the medical consciousness, then the relevance of some of the most natural healing methods should come to be appreciated. Whether we will ever be able to use technological oscillators, on their own, with the necessary subtlety to correct the most serious conditions is open to doubt. The only instrument capable of complete and immediate diagnosis and treatment is the human organism. For most of us, this is just a potentiality deep down in the psyche – although in continuous use at the unconscious level in all close relationships. But the ultimate goal for therapists is the conscious healing of another through simple physical contact and direct psychical understanding. That this does sometimes happen today, there is little doubt; and with new insight into our own energy fields, such healing can become part of rational knowledge.

10. General Reflections

Many years have passed since I drafted the first chapter. Much has happened that is greatly to be welcomed. The rigidity and dogmatism of an older generation of scientists are being replaced by a willingness to discuss new possibilities. Much that was considered naturally absurd on a materialist-monist basis, or on a strict 4-dimensional deterministic basis, or through the limited perceptions of quantum theorists and geneticists, is now thought worthy of serious intellectual effort. The reductionist, caught in an impossible position of having to accept his ideas and theories as either genetically predetermined, or the result of pure chance, is being forced towards more commonsense notions of mental freedom. Without rational, conscious choice, there can be no science.

Slowly we are moving away from the idea of an all-embracing scientific body of knowledge, where nothing is plausible unless clearly within a certain narrow theoretical framework. This is not to suggest there is no place for some limited dogmatism. In the practical approach to new problems, there is much to be said for exploring thoroughly a specific hypothesis before moving on to alternatives. If there is a half-promising theory around, better to proceed for a while on the assumption that it has some intrinsic merit, if only in defining the problems more clearly. There are certainly dangers in rushing from one exotic concept to another.

Not that this is ever likely to be an affliction of the major scientific schools. They find it so difficult to let go when whole careers have been devoted to one specific line of thought. Indirectly, because so much builds up beyond the realms of orthodox theory, this encourages the development of supernatural categories that preclude the possibility of causal understanding. The interest in Eastern thought, particularly Yoga concepts, stems both from our disenchantment with things supernatural, and our frustration with scientific 'certainty'.

To me, one of the more interesting changes in outlook in the life-sciences over the last ten years has been the relatively unpublicised move away from the static concept of *homeostasis* in living organisms, to something more dynamic and cyclic. Under homeostasis, it was assumed that fundamental body parameters such as temperature, blood flow, hormone secretion, water balance, etc., were held in a state of equilibrium by the diencephalon of the brain core. With more subtle measurement, this we now know to be incorrect, or at least somewhat misleading, in that all the major parameters of body activity have definite rhythms. The important periodic cycles seem to follow the outer cosmic events, particularly the daily rotation of the earth. These *circadian* cycles correlate most naturally with elec-tromagnetic effects of the geomagnetic field, thus encouraging scien-tists to reconsider their previous dismissal of medieval concepts about man reflecting the outer world in his emotional life. When we take into account, not the absolute smallness of our own electromagnetic field, but rather that the earth's field around the body is about a million times greater than our own, then this all looks very reasonable and intelligible.

This type of change is also reflected in the new organic agriculture, based not only on internal chemistry, but on the outer energy rhythms. Slowly, particle and molecular concepts in the life sciences are being complemented by wave and field theories. In the coming century, I think that scientific rationalisation will be increasingly con-cerned with the 'musical' aspects of energy, with frequency, amp-litude, resonance, and dissonance as fundamental factors in any physical structure. Even in the harder sciences of physics and chemis-try, I would envisage such a process, with chemical and subatomic bonding organised, not through the fleeting existence of mediating particles, but by an orderly and musical arrangement of frequency. There has even been quite recently some tongue-in-cheek speculation about a musical interpretation for the genetic bases of DNA.

Of all the controversies raging today, evolutionary theory con-tinues to hold the centre stage – as it has done for much of the last hundred years. The controversy exists at many different levels. For the evolutionists, there is the internal controversy of nature versus nurture, between natural selection and adaptive change, between survival of the fittest and creative modification – questions that seem-ingly get resolved at one point, only to be brought back later for further discussion. At another level, the gradualist Darwinian thesis is challenged by those of the *punctuated equilibrium* school involving discontinuity and sudden quantum changes. Dubrov's thesis relating genetic changes to reversals of geomagnetic polarity every half-million years or so comes partly into this category, although recognis-ing the possibility of more continuous change through the daily effects of earth and solar fields.

Today, the evolutionists are facing a renewed challenge from the

Creationists, who return somewhat better informed than their nineteenth century counterparts on the weaknesses of evolutionary evidence. Then, to all except the most committed Darwinians, there is the fundamental problem of man. Is he part of animal evolution? Or are the unique mental, conscious, and creative abilities of man in some way distinct from evolutionary and hereditary processes? The belief in man as a special creation has the deepest religious roots.

There has been, in my opinion, a tendency to take evolutionary theory far too seriously and dogmatically. With our present levels of understanding, it can hardly be said to have the status of a scientific hypothesis that we can begin to affirm or refute by laboratory testing. It is more an attempt to put biology into a scientific context where problems may be defined more precisely, and a suitable language for discussing these problems generated.

Most of the early terminology, with words like gene or character, was suitably ambiguous, no one having much idea what they might eventually come to mean. A gene was a mysterious organiser that controlled a character, such as an organ, or a function, or a chemical colour. Today, a gene has a chemical definition in terms of DNA sequences in the cell nucleus that generate proteins. But character remains as vague as ever. Some assume it covers mental abilities and emotional disposition. Others reserve it for anatomical description, although it is impossible to isolate out one part from a multitude of other systems. An eye, for instance, is connected through the nerves and the blood with almost all parts of the body.

Half a century before Darwin and Wallace gave us their ideas, Jean-Baptiste Lamarck presented an evolutionary theory in much less controversial terms, and based on ideas that non-biologists could feel reasonably comfortable with. Although Anglo-Saxons have tried to argue that he borrowed his main ideas from Erasmus Darwin, grandfather of Charles Darwin, many now accept Lamarck as the true founder of the modern evolutionary thesis. However, in his time, Lamarck was not a major force in the academic world, and did not have, as Darwin did, a powerful body of high academics zealously defending and propagating his ideas.

Beginning from the spontaneous generation of the first cell, Lamarck envisaged a purposive evolutionary process developing through the intrinsic needs of the organism. Through use and movement, organic material expanded and adapted; through disuse, it atrophied. Thus each organism developed itself according to its situation, and passed its existing characteristics on to the next generation. To Lamarck, the word 'chance' only expressed our ignorance of causes, and this still remains the most basic objection to chance mutational theory.

As one seldom finds any material relating to what Lamarck actually said, it might be useful here to give Lamarck's four laws of organic development (summarised in English by H. G. Cannon).

1. Life, by its own force, tends continually to increase the volume of every living body and to extend the dimensions of its parts, up to a limit which it imposes.

2. The production of a new organ in an animal body results from a new need (*besoin*) which continues to make itself felt, and from a new movement that this need brings and maintains.

3. The development and effectiveness of organs are proportional to the use of these organs.

4. Everything acquired or changed during an individual's lifetime is preserved by heredity and transmitted to that individual's progeny.

The first law, like Newton's first law of motion, is a very general statement saying nothing in particular. However, the suggestion of vitalism, of a separate life-force, would not find favour in the academic schools. The second and third laws few would dispute, being very much part of our own natural experience of life. The fourth law has been the source of great controversy this century, and the word 'everything' must be a serious overstatement.

Many nineteenth century evolutionists accepted the idea of Lamarckian inheritance of acquired characteristics, and Darwin himself changed his mind on the subject more than once. Darwin's instinct was to try to base all species development on chance genetic mutations and combinations, together with the assumption that the germ plasm was somehow sealed off from the rest of the system, and remained unchanged throughout life. However, when it was realised that a simple blending of male and female characteristics would lead to uniformity, not diversity, Darwin's theory of natural selection in its original form had to be abandoned. There was no way to account for new species on a genetic averaging basis; and at the turn of the century, some degree of Lamarckian inheritance had to be assumed.

Fortunately for Darwin, Mendel's paper was rediscovered in 1900, 35 years after publication, and seemed to solve the blending problem – in theory at least. Mendel showed that some simple characteristics of plants did not average out, but were either one or the other. On such a binary either-or basis, much greater variety is allowed for; and over the course of the next two decades, neo-Darwinism, incorporating Mendelian genetics, became the orthodox force. Thus the postulate that the germ plasm was unaffected by acquired characteristics could once more be safely assumed, and everything again reduced to chance. Useful changes, with survival value, enhanced a species; other changes led to extinction.

Those who held to the Lamarckian view of a creative evolutionary process gradually became the new heretics, and the enemies of true science – i.e. Western, and specifically Anglo-Saxon science. Carefully protected by academic reductionists, positivists, and monists, the Darwin thesis in which the greedy and most ruthless survive, found its natural home in capitalist society. It was the socialists and radicals who wanted to hold on to Lamarck, believing in some purposive development, and refusing to reject altruistic ideas about helping others to survive for the general good of the species.

Today, the debate is much more technical. Neo-Darwinians point to the DNA chemistry which suggests that the genetic processes are not reversible – that is, the process from DNA to RNA to protein cannot react back on the original DNA. Neo-Lamarckians argue this may not be the case, and that there could be a reverse process through the immunological system. However, with no understanding about how a set of genes might create an overall form, such arguments have little merit. Concepts of gene strategy become more speculative every year, now involving embryonic 'master genes' that conveniently switch themselves on and off according to the particular stages of growth reached.

A most fundamental point made in this book is that, if we think of genes, not as static *on-off* groups of chemicals, but as *oscillators with coherent frequency properties*, then there is no inherent theoretical problem about embryonic growth. *An ordered set of oscillators will produce a consistent patterning of material. It will ensure that the formation of new structures will occur according to a definite time sequence. It will create patterns of rhythmic activity throughout the organism. It can account for degeneration and ageing, as well as the initial growth patterns. It can explain in principle both the cell formation and the whole-body formation.*

Apart from basic frequency characteristics, we have seen that genes have specific energy polarisations that result in complementary D and L geometrical molecular forms. With thousands of genes, or segments of DNA, in each chromosome, the detailed variations through polarising factors are virtually unlimited. In Dubrov's thesis, the complex and continuously varying geomagnetic field affects the genetic polarisation at the very beginning of each individual life. Also, occasional north-south reversals in the static component of the earth's field have a fundamental effect on the different species, strengthening some and weakening others.

Does this then throw any light on the central controversy between the chance mutation philosophy of the Darwinians, and purposeful evolutionary processes developing from basic needs of Lamarck? Is one more correct that the other, or can they both be right, as many Victorians assumed?

In Darwinian theory, it is assumed that, while most chance mutations (through high-frequency radiation or direct chemical action) will be destructive, the odd change here and there will be useful and have survival value. To most outsiders, this sounds unlikely and implausible; and it is of interest that such an idea has had to be carefully 'nurtured' through esoteric statistical argument by high academic specialists. The gut feeling of many is that, in some sense, Lamarck will be proved to be nearer the truth of things because of his more commonsense approach involving an inherent ability of life to develop itself and adapt to different conditions.

At the human level, we know that by exercise and will-power, the body can be consciously developed; by neglect and abuse, it can be seriously impaired. If Lamarck were on the right lines in that we pass on to the next generation some, or just a little of our non-inherited development, then evolutionary theory could be made generally intelligible to all thinking people. Purposeful things like special muscles, webbed feet, pouches for the young, long necks, unusual beaks, which make little sense in Darwinian terms, can be theoretically understood on a Lamarckian basis.

Darwinians will say that the supporters of Lamarck have just failed to come up with some hard evidence. First, artificial amputations were tried, like cutting tails, to see if the resulting forms of later generations involved suggestions of such operations. This however was not really what Lamarck was getting at. One had to look for natural processes, natural adaptations over a lengthy period of time, and it became increasingly clear that Lamarck's hypothesis would be extremely difficult to test on a laboratory basis – not that there is anything to test on a random Darwinian basis. There has also been the added complication that the biological laboratories of the West have been under the control, and very severe control, of the Darwinians for most of this century, making it difficult to carry out experiments that might support Lamarck's thesis.

Arthur Koestler, who always favoured Lamarck's viewpoint, has written in depth about the tragic life of Paul Kammerer, an unusual scientist whose work aroused great interest at the beginning of this century. Various specimens, suggesting inheritance of acquired characters, were studied over many years by European and American researchers. Then, with Kammerer near the end of his life, impoverished in Austria after the Great War, and with only one specimen left for factual evidence and that in bad condition, the biologists found in it a fraudulent black spot injected with Indian ink – the spot of course being the evidence of Lamarckian-type inheritance. All who knew Kammerer personally, and had followed his experiments over the years, were convinced that, through a number of possible motives, an opponent of Kammerer had injected the ink to discredit him. But the Darwinians took the line that Kammerer was a fraud, regardless of all the ingenious breeding experiments that had been previously accepted as genuine. Kammerer's death, assumed to be suicide, followed shortly after.

I have no intention of entering this complex controversy, except for pointing out some of the problems likely to be encountered by anyone experimenting on this basis. As in psychical research, there may come a point when further experimentation is rather pointless, people having already prejudged the issue.

Scientists today are more likely to be swayed by some theoretical basis for changes in the germ cell DNA. And what now seems eminently worth exploring is *whether or not low-frequency electromagnetic fields can change the structure of a gene or a chromosome*. What we can affirm, without ambiguity, is that as the structure changes or develops, so the total electromagnetic field pattern will be modified. Thus for example, areas of hardened and thickened skin arising from contact with a rocky surface, would effect a change in the morphological field. The question then is whether or not such a change could react back on the germ cells. *This is the crucial Lamarckian question.*

At this stage of our knowledge, one cannot give a definitive answer to this, although there are several positive indicators. In general theoretical terms, we can surmise that such fields, with extremely low energy intensity, are unlikely to affect the basic molecular content of the DNA. But it is quite possible that they may affect the polarisation of molecules and genes; and it also possible that they may modify the way nuclear material breaks up into chromosomes when the cell is about to divide. With either one of these possibilities, we would have a possible mechanism for genetic change on a Lamarckian basis.

As was mentioned in the previous chapter discussing Dubrov's thesis, there is some experimental evidence that the geomagnetic field modifies genes and chromosomes. There is for instance a gene mutation of the insect Adalia which changes the wing colour from red to black. Such changes correlate quite closely with the geomagnetic field. Similarly, inversions of the X-chromosomes of the fruit-fly have been shown to follow the GMF fluctuations. Not that this proves a direct causal link between one and the other; but these and other studies are beginning to broaden our horizons about the nature of genetic change.

We have already seen in this book how low-frequency fields can affect mental states, physiological functions, bone structure, and general patterning processes. The germ plasm is certainly not insulated from these fields which permeate the whole body. The view now of a number of researchers is that these fields affect directly a larger structure like the cell membrane, which has unusual electromagnetic properties, and this in turn has some subtle effect on the nuclear material. Others would be more specific, relating it to the unusual water structures in the cell membrane, these being sensitive to low-frequency fields.

In all such discussion, it is very necessary to keep in mind our ignorance about what, apart from making proteins, genes are actually meant to do, or to control. In educational circles, for instance, it is now quite commonplace to hear behaviourists talking about children working to their 'genetic potential' – thus implying that their mental ability is directly related to their inherited genes. Such limiting and damaging assumptions, with obvious class and racial implications, easily become part of the natural climate of thought.

Then again, are physical skills, as distinct from physical structure, controlled by gene patterns? Are we, in other words, to make a basic distinction between the development of an organ, and the ability to use the organ? Karl Popper is one of those who thinks so, this being in line with his 3-world concept recently put forward after his final disenchantment with monism. Some degree of dualism, or pluralism, he thinks may be useful in genetics.

In discussing genes and inherited characteristics, my own view is that we are not directly concerned with things of the mind or the memory. Great creative ability comes from all walks of life, and from all races. Early evolutionists like T. H. Huxley could not conceive of black people ever attaining anything approaching the Anglo-Saxon mental levels, but they have been proved completely wrong. Many outstanding people have simple origins, with no history of great intelligence and learning. This applies to scientists, artists, composers, statesmen, and people in any field of activity one cares to look at. And emotional tendencies, to my mind, have just as little connection with inheritance. Not that the physical aspect has no effect on these, for an unhealthy body will affect the emotional tone and the mental concentration. But given normal physical health, the mind and the emotions seem detached to a large extent from the inherited factors.

Many in the academic world today would welcome a move away from Darwinism. A theory that postulates pure chance in the development from single cells to the human species of billions of cells can only be a stepping-stone towards a causal biological science. Many have pointed out how, with a minimum of purposeful prompting, evolutionary theory could be presented so much more plausibly.

But evolutionists have been a fierce breed of the species, ruthlessly attacking both the outsiders who found their materialist-monism untenable, and the insiders with alternative heresies like Lamarck. No greater champion have they had than Ernst Haeckel, who while writing interestingly and informatively on embryology, solved all the social, political, and religious problems as well. He writes of the "struggle for the final triumph of truth", that "evolution has now pressed on to its final victory"; and how "the eternal iron laws that rule the evolution of the whole cosmos control our own life".

As he got older, there was no softening of Haeckel's views – very much the reverse. Man was part of the animal world, and to realise his full potential, he had to accept the brutal ways of nature. The Germans were a superior race, and had to ensure that their genetic superiority was not polluted by alien species, such as the Jews who had emigrated from Russia.

Nor had it to be polluted by those who were born weak, or ill-formed, or handicapped. And of those who had a 'hereditary bias towards mysticism', he says that

It is to be explained phylogenetically by inheritance from pre-historic bar-barians and savages, in whom the earliest religious ideas were wholly domi-nated by animism and fetichism.

He never tired of attacking the concept of the freedom of the will, maintaining that

the great struggle between the determinist and the indeterminist, between the opponent and sustainer of the freedom of the will, has ended today, after more than two thousand years, completely in favour of the determinist. The human will has no more freedom than that of the higher animals, from which it differs only in degree and not in kind.

Thus all liberal thought, and ideas of social democracy, were to be despised, especially as they had no place in the natural and biological order of things. The only necessary individual freedom, it would seem, was the freedom for Haeckel to pontificate on any matter under the sun.

Haeckel formed the German Monist League which became a very influential social force at the beginning of the century, encouraging German nationalism, and arguing the need for a colonisation prog-ramme. Such efforts found their ultimate consummation in the fascist and Nazi movements which attempted to establish a 'naturalistic' religion based largely on Haeckel's evolutionary monism.

Not that it would be fair to put all the blame on the Monist League. Some who belonged to it were pacifists, or socialists, or Marxists. But

Haeckel, through his commanding personality and best-selling books, was the dominant influence. Strangely, he had a long association with Rudolf Steiner. In their younger days, both had similar evolutionary viewpoints, and both were keen to establish more naturalistic ideas in which rational thought rather than inherited dogma played the major part. But after 1900, their viewpoints began to diverge, and by the end of their lives, they were almost at opposite poles – one absorbed in Christian concepts, and making extreme efforts to look after the most disadvantaged; the other deciding that Christianity was an absolute disaster for modern man, weakening the will to strive, to compete, and if necessary, to conquer.

To Haeckel, and to most evolutionists of his time – Wallace being a most notable exception – anything dualist, pluralist, idealist, and vitalist was just so much metaphysical nonsense. There were the great laws of physics (now somewhat changed), and the great law of evolutionary development (still fiercely debated). In the 4-dimensional universe, all was predetermined. There was no soul, no freedom, no immortal life. Even though they could put forward only the most speculative ideas about embryological development, there was an almost terrifying certainty that there was absolutely no alternative to their version of the truth.

In passing, I would add that, looking into their theories of vertebrate development, one finds a certain mechanical quaintness. Read, for instance, Herbert Spencer's attempt to explain the somite sectioning of a vertebrate. Summarising his rather long argument, perhaps a little unfairly, the reasoning was essentially that by pushing a length of pliable material this way and that, it eventually broke up under the strain into separate segments. How it always happened in such regular proportions, how it naturally fitted in with spinal nerve connections, how in fact such a random process could produce the most sophisticated control system in the living world, these were matters for another day. However, to be fair to Herbert Spencer, he was no Haeckel, and wrote perceptively on many subjects.

Evolutionary theory will remain only a speculative hypothesis until we begin to understand something causal about embryology. It is of such generality, and so lacking in specificity, that it can be used in almost any context of human thought. The Darwinian aspects of struggle and survival can be appealed to by capitalists and fascists. The altruistic aspects for the good of the species have religious implications. The purposeful aspects of Lamarck are much the sort of thing modern democrats and socialists want to hear. And one of the very fascinating aspects about it all is the way the changing *ideas* about natural evolution develop, sometimes mirroring, sometimes reversing, the character of the processes they try to describe.

Science, particularly Anglo-Saxon or Anglo-German science, has been dominated for a century or more by men like Haeckel – intimidating people who insist all their research workers share their aims and philosophy. They have made the government and administration of science more feudal than democratic, more theological than free-thinking. All approaches to knowledge must be given their seal of approval before being considered worthy of serious effort.

Not that temperament is the only problem. There are major difficulties with the modern tendency to classify scientists as either theoretical or experimental. For example, when one demonstrates with a simple oscillator (figure 9.2) a basic electrical property of acupoints, the theoretical man so often feels incompetent to assess what is happening. Then without definite guidance from the theoretician, the experimentalist will consider he is just wasting his time. There is also the tendency, in this great electronic age, to overlook the simple experiment with simple equipment.

Sometimes modern theories get in the way. Quantum theorists, for instance, have pointed out how difficult it would be for a human being either to receive or send signals at very low frequencies because of the enormously long aerial required – like that used in submarine communication. Preoccupied with advanced theory, it is easy to forget very elementary knowledge of magnetic fields. Using the same simple oscillator, one has only to wave the magnetic coil near any radio set to hear the audio signal. No specific aerial is required, the audio circuits of the radio being activated by simple magnetic induction. Similarly in the body: if there already exist circuits, or oscillators, or nerve cells resonating at low frequencies, then they will respond to similar frequencies from an external field. Low-frequency phenomena are not easily conceived in photon terms.

In the formation of living structures, the problem has been to get embryologists and geneticists away from the notion of a purely *chemical* explanation of everything. There is no logical reason why they should expect an explanation on these lines because chemistry is not essentially geometrical. Agreed that chemistry is now more concerned with geometry, but this is descriptive rather than causal. The present academic approach to morphogenesis is rather reminiscent of the medieval scholars who insisted that all planetary motions must be described in circles – so requiring a very complex edifice of circular motions imposed on other circular motions to get some reasonable approximation to observational evidence.

We all know that consistent yet changing patterns are created by consistent waveforms. Demonstrating such a concept, either practically or theoretically, is, as we have seen, a very straightforward business. Whether or not the specific frequency patterns suggested in this book are basically on the right lines for the human vertebrate structure, this is of no great consequence. The important thing is that such an approach has the potentiality to solve fundamental problems. Conversely, it is very difficult to conceive any other approach, any other type of formative process, that has such a potentiality.

The problems of developing new approaches are part technical, part cultural, part psychological. Perhaps most important of all, the concept of an all-embracing monism has been exceptionally appealing, suiting both Anglo-Saxon science and theology. Thus in the 4-dimensional deterministic continuum, plus an optional Creator, scientists and theologians have been able to live comfortably together this century. The controversies in the academic world between religion and evolutionary theory have been, if not resolved, at least suitably accommodated. Evolutionary processes can be seen as part of God's design, or not, as the case may be.

Haeckel was at least reasonably consistent and honest in his attitude towards Christianity, uncompromisingly rejecting all the humbug of those who would claim to be both Christian and capitalist at the same time. He did recognise that survival of the fittest was the diametrical opposite of loving one's enemies. And as for giving away all one's material possessions, he said that on that basis, having had half of their colonies stolen by the British, the Germans should offer them the other half.

Christian ideals such as we find in the Sermon on the Mount have no natural place in the Anglo-Saxon aggressive and confrontational culture. They are just tolerated, and perhaps slightly ameliorate the worst excesses of capitalist philosophy. Some would regard them as having relevance only to personal relationships, not to the great issues of state and philosophy. 'All you need is love' is such a simplistic outlook to most, who have to spend their lives grubbing for money and outwitting the opposition. By all means, it is argued, let the uneducated masses find what comfort they can in such primitive ideas, but leave the educated élite alone to make the real decisions in the real world.

The Christian-capitalist contradictions continuously destabilise our society, and often tear us apart individually. Now, with the emergence of new and extreme forms of Social Darwinism, there is a strong chance that we are likely in the comparatively near future to blow ourselves and the rest of the world to bits – either through accident or predetermined design. We have certainly made all the necessary provisions for doing just this, with weapons' systems primed to go into action at a moment's notice. There are no Christian feelings towards those who, for better or worse, have opted to order their societies on a more co-operative and communal basis. Hard science and hard politics are now the order of the day.

Such hard attitudes follow from artificial limitations imposed on the mind, including of course the assumption that the mind itself is no more than some chemical function governed by predictable or random forces. But if we regard the world of the mind as over and beyond the world of the body, then we can rationally embrace the concept of free will. Moreover, by taking such a viewpoint in harmony with our intuitive sense of things, we automatically reinforce it.

The alternative would seem to be a pathetic resignation to what is happening all around us. With present attitudes, we will continue busily destroying the natural environment. We will continue fanatically devising ever more lethal weapons of mass destruction. We will continue to encourage a hopeless subservience to drugs and various inhumane medical practices. In the pre-determined 4-dimensional continuum, the dimensions of love, and freedom, and creativity, are conspicuously absent. Ultimately it is all particles randomly reacting with each other. If we feed our children on such a diet, what can we expect?

I recently received a charming little book by the American scientist and writer, Samuel McLaughlin, who makes the most natural case, without esoteric argument or mathematics, for a world view that does include the higher dimensions necessary to freedom and choice. In his 6-dimensional universe, there are an infinity of possible 4-dimensional worlds, with each dimension, or partial dimension, adding to our perceptual power. From the dot, to the line, to the surface, to the space, to the space-time, and then on to variations of space-time, he outlines something not at odds with 4-dimensional determinism, but simply extending it to involve the free activity of the mind and will. This is a 'cumulative' approach to dimensions, nicely complementing the dualist approach of chapter 4.

In his introduction, he says

We all have an intuitive understanding of dimensions, and we need only some terminology, and a plan of organisation for the topic, in order for this knowledge to become conscious. The properties of the six dimensions of the universe, and the relations of these dimensions to human consciousness, are the fundamental facts of existence, and should be taught to every child in elementary school.

Considering first our normal waking perception, he points out that there can never be any instantaneous 3-dimensional perception of the world, our senses and nerve pathways making everything time-dependent. We look out on the world through a time-window, which as discussed in chapter 7, is something of the order of one tenth of a second in our basic level of consciousness. At different levels of consciousness, this time-slice varies, when minutes may seem like seconds, and hours like minutes. Think also how much activity just one second involves at the atomic level. There is no basic difficulty in conceiving a timeless state of consciousness involving the whole of the past, present, and future, and which would be the total determinate 4-dimensional world.

So, observing the fall of a raindrop, an extended consciousness with wider time-slices would perceive a line of raindrops – the actual path of the raindrop. Its trajectory constitutes a perceptual projection of part of the 4-dimensional world, representing something between 3 and 4 dimensions. If we then extend this space-time to a surface or plane, we move to the fifth dimension containing different possibilities, yet related to the here and now. Then, expanding this surface to a solid, we explore all the possibilities. In this 6-dimensional continuum, we may think of the 3-dimensional projection as a point, the 4-dimensional projection as one specific line or set of possibilities, and higher dimensions giving the infinity of variations of the 4-dimensional projections.

An inspired quotation from P. D. Ouspensky in his book *A New Model of the Universe* states all this most eloquently.

If we try to imagine the actualisation of all the possibilities of the present moment, then of the next moment, and so on, we shall feel the world growing infinitely, incessantly multiplying by itself and becoming immeasurably rich and utterly unlike the flat and limited world we have pictured to ourselves up to this moment. Having imagined this infinite variety we shall feel a 'taste' of infinity for a moment and shall understand how inadequate and impossible it is to approach the problem of time with earthly measures. We shall understand what an infinite richness of time going in all directions is necessary for the actualisation of all the possibilities that arise each moment. And we shall understand that the very idea of arising and disappearing possibilities is created by the human mind, because otherwise it would burst and perish from a single contact with the infinite actualisation.

Our problem today is whether we can begin to accept, to realise the possibilities of such transcendent thought; or whether we are to be content with the genetic conditioning, the law of the jungle, the random yet predetermined world of the scientific monists.

I am pessimistic about our Western, particularly Anglo-Saxon culture. I somehow doubt whether it can resolve its inherent contradictions, with its strong religious emphasis on communal and caring activity, and its even stronger Darwinian emphasis on competition, confrontation, and struggle against each other. One looks longingly towards the gentler East, to Indian society where religion and philosophy and social life share common aims and ideals. Without us, they would certainly survive for more millenia, living close to nature, close to each other, and aware of the higher conscious levels towards which man may aspire. Many in the West are beginning to yearn for such an existence, working more selflessly in smaller communities; but in our present ordered and machine-dependent society, such attempts require a level of courage and persistence that few possess. Perhaps only some natural catastrophe might save us from our present aggressive and suicidal paths.

Many are now profoundly dissatisfied with our Western *certainties*. But trying to emulate ancient cultures, however enlightened, seems not a realistic option. We can only work from where we are. Our religion, in its broadest sense, does at least recognise the wonderful mystery of each individual life. Here we are, born into a world of perplexing strangeness, not knowing where we are going, and perceiving through the senses only the tiniest fraction of all that is happening. Why so many scientists find it impossible to consider the possibility of being born equally mysteriously into some other life, some other body, some other environment, I do not know.

Yet while we have only limited ability to *perceive* through the senses, we have the ability to *conceive* the whole cosmos in all its dimensions and energy manifestations. The notion of consciousness, which is able to conceive of itself, is at the heart of everything. A universe unobserved, without consciousness, is impossible to conceive; nor is one able to conceive of no universe, of nothing. Between knowing and not-knowing, our finite minds are energised into ceaseless activity creating worlds of form and order from the infinite complexities of energy. Consciousness is not a product of atoms and cells; rather it is consciousness that creates the possibility of conceiving atoms and cells.

At this critical point in human evolution, there is a sense of mankind coming of age, and a new conscious acceptance of a responsibility for ourselves, our society, and the whole planet. But there is also the sense of adventure in our evolving personal freedom. It is through the *uncertainties* of the future, and with new quests along uncharted paths, that we will grow, and understand, and experience the abundance of life.

Bibliography

Adams, George, *Physical and Ethereal Spaces*, Rudolf Steiner Press, 1965.

Aspden, Harold, *Physics Unified*, Sabberton Publications, 1980.

Austin, Mary, *Acupuncture Therapy*, Turnstone Books, 1974.

Becker, Robert O and Marino, Andrew A, *Electromagnetism and Life*, State University of New York Press, 1982.

Blair, Lawrence, *Rhythms of Vision*, Granada Publishing, 1976.

Blavatsky, H P, *Isis Unveiled*, Theosophical Publishing Society, 1910.

Bouquet, A C, *Comparative Religion*, Penguin Books, 1956.

Bowler, Peter J, *Evolution. The History of an Idea*, University of California Press, 1984.

Brillouin, Léon, *Relativity Re-examined*, Academic Press, 1970.

Brunton, Paul, *The Hidden Teaching beyond Yoga*, Rider & Co., 1969. *The Wisdom of the Overself*, Rider & Co., 1968.

Burkhardt, Richard W, *The Spirit of System. Lamarck and Evolutionary Biology*, Harvard University Press, 1977.

Buranelli, Vincent, *The Wizard from Vienna*, Peter Owen, 1976.

Cannon, Graham H, *Lamarck and Modern Genetics*, Manchester University Press, 1959.

Cerminara, Gina, *Many Mansions*, Neville Spearman, 1967.

Choain, Jean, *La Voie Rationale de la Médecine Chinoise*, Editions S.L.E.L. Lille, 1957.

Crookall, Robert, *The Study and Practice of Astral Projection*, Aquarian Press, 1961.

Danielou, Alain, *Yoga. The Method of Reintegration*, Johnson Publications, 1973.

Dirac, Paul, *Directions in Physics*, John Wiley & Sons, 1978.

Dubrov, Aleksandr Petrovich, *The Geomagnetic Field and Life*, Plenum Press, 1978.

Eccles, John C, *The Understanding of the Brain*, McGraw-Hill, 1977.

Einstein, Albert, *Ideas and Opinions*, Souvenir Press, 1973.

Eisendrath, Craig, *The Unifying Moment*, Harvard University Press, 1971.

Ford, K W, *The World of Elementary Particles*, Blaisdell Publishing Company, 1958.

Frankfort, H, *Before Philosophy*, Penguin Books, 1951.

Garrett, Eileen, *My Life as a Search for the Meaning of Mediumship*, Rider & Co., 1939.

Gasman, Daniel, *The Scientific Origins of National Socialism*, Macdonald & Co., 1971.

Goethe, Johann Wolfgang von, *Theory of Colours*, Frank Cass, 1967.

Haeckel, Ernst, *The Riddle of the Universe*, Watts & Co., 1900.

Harwood, A C, *The Faithful Thinker*, Hodder and Stoughton, 1961.

Hatton, J L S, *The Theory of the Imaginary in Geometry*, Cambridge University Press, 1926.
Heisenberg, Werner, *Physics and Philosophy*, George Allen & Unwin, 1963.
   Physics and Beyond, George Allen & Unwin, 1971.
Hessey, J D, *Colour in the Treatment of Disease*, Rider & Co., 1929.
Humphreys, Christmas, *Buddhism*, Penguin Books, 1951.
Iamblichus, *Life of Pythagoras*, John M Watkins, 1965.
Iverson, Jeffrey, *More Lives than One*, Souvenir Press, 1976.
Jacobi, Jolande, *The Psychology of C.G. Jung*, Routledge & Kegan Paul, 1975.
James, William, *The Principles of Psychology*, Dover Publications, 1950.
   A Pluralistic Universe, Harvard University Press, 1977.
   Psychical Research, Chatto & Windus, 1961.
Jenny, Hans, *Cymatics*, Basilius Press, 1966.
Jung, C G, *Modern Man in Search of a Soul*, Routledge & Kegan Paul, 1978.
Koestler, Arthur, *Janus: A Summing Up*, Pan Books, 1979.
Laing, R D, *The Divided Self*, Penguin Books, 1965.
Lashley, K S, *The Neuro-Psychology of Lashley: Selected Papers*, McGraw-Hill, 1960.
Leadbeater, C W, *The Chakras*, Theosophical Publishing House, 1977.
Lindlahr, Henry, *Philosophy of National Therapeutics*, Maidstone Osteopathic Clinic, 1975.
Lodge, Sir Oliver, *My Philosophy*, Ernest Benn, 1933.
Mann, Felix, *Acupuncture: The Ancient Chinese Art of Healing*, Heinemann Medical Books, 1971.
   Scientific Aspects of Acupuncture, Heinemann Medical Books, 1977.
Mann, W E, *Orgone, Reich and Eros*, Simon and Schuster, 1973.
McLaughlin, Samuel Clarke, *On Feeling Good*, Autumn Press, 1978.
Mishlove, Jeffrey, *The Roots of Consciousness*, Random House, 1975.
Muldoon, S V, *The Projection of the Astral Body*, Rider & Co., 1929.
Myers, Frederic, *Human Personality and its Survival of Bodily Death*, Longmans, Green, and Co., 1907.
Nunez, P L, *Electric Fields of the Brain*, Oxford University Press, 1981.
Ohashi, Otaru, *Shiatsu*, George Allen & Unwin, 1977.
O'Neill, John J, *Prodigal Genius. The Life of Nikola Tesla*, Neville Spearman, 1968.
Ornstein, Robert, *The Psychology of Consciousness*, Jonathan Cape, 1975.
Ouspensky, P D, *A New Model of the Universe*, Routledge & Kegan Paul, 1931.
Packard, Alpheus S, *Lamarck, The Founder of Evolution*, Longmans, Green, and Co., 1901.
Penfield, Wilder, *The Cerebral Cortex of Man*, Macmillan, 1957.
   Speech and Brain-mechanisms, Princeton University Press, 1959.
   The Mystery of the Mind, Princeton University Press, 1975.
Polanyi, Michael, *The Tacit Dimension*, Routledge & Kegan Paul, 1967.
Polkinghorne, J C, *The Particle Play*, W H Freeman, 1979.
Popper, Karl R, *Objective Knowledge. An Evolutionary Approach*, Oxford University Press, 1972.
Prigogine, Ilya, *Self-organisation in Non-equilibrium Systems*, John Wiley & Sons, 1977.
Reich, Wilhelm, *Selected Writings*, Vision Press, 1961.
Sannella, Lee, *Kundalini – Psychosis or Transcendence?*, published privately, San Francisco, 1976.
Schreiber, F R, *Sybil*, Penguin Books, 1975.

Sheppard, Asher R and Eisenbud, Merril, *Biological Effects of Electric and Magnetic Fields of Extremely Low Frequency*, New York University Press, 1977.

Sheldrake, Rupert, *A New Science of Life*, Blond & Briggs, 1981.

Sherrington, Sir Charles, *Man on his Nature*, Cambridge University Press, 1951.

Sinnett, A P, *Esoteric Buddhism*, Theosophical Publishing House, 1883.
The Rationale of Mesmerism, Kegan Paul, 1892.

Steiner, Rudolf, *At the Gates of Spiritual Science*, Rudolf Steiner Press, 1970.
Man: Hieroglyph of the Universe, Rudolf Steiner Press, 1972.

Sugrue, Thomas, *There is a River*, A.R.E. Press, Virginia, 1973.

Tart, Charles, *Altered States of Consciousness*, John Wiley & Sons, 1969.

Tenforde, T S (editor), *Magnetic Field Effects on Biological Systems*, Plenum Press, 1979.

Thompson, D'Arcy, *On Growth and Form*, Cambridge University Press, 1917.

Tomkins, P and Bird, C, *The Secret Life of Plants*, Penguin Books, 1975.

Turing, A M, *The Chemical Basis of Morphogenesis*, Philosophical transactions of the Royal Society 1952.

Wallace, Alfred Russell, *My Life*, Chapman & Hall, 1908.

Walter, W Grey, *The Living Brain*, Duckworth, 1953.

Wambach, Helen, *Life before Life*, Bantam Books, 1979.

Woodroffe, Sir John, *The Serpent Power*, Luzac & Co., 1919.

Worsley, J R, *Traditional Chinese Acupuncture*, Element Books, 1982.

Index